SHAKESPEARE AND MEDICINE

BY

R. R. SIMPSON
M.B., Ch.B., F.R.C.S., F.R.C.S.Ed.

E. & S. LIVINGSTONE LTD.
EDINBURGH AND LONDON
1959

Printed by
PICKERING & INGLIS LTD.,
Glasgow
Printed in Great Britain

PREFACE

L
ITTLE that is new can be written about Shakespeare; and certainly no commentator can approach this subject without being aware of the immense debt he owes to the great variety of writers who have preceded him. Some of that debt can be recognised as due to particular books, or articles, or teachers; but much of it remains vaguely in the mind as being owed to forgotten or unknown or unrecognised sources—an attitude formed in the mind of the writer after years of familiarity with the writings on Shakespeare. It is not that one is unwilling to acknowledge the source of the debt; it is simply that from 'l'embarras de richesse' one fails to recognise where or when the nuances of one's opinions evolved, matured and took form.

With persons it is easy. To Peter Alexander, for his interest and encouragement over the years, I give priority in my most grateful thanks. To Raymond L. Brett, for reading the manuscript and for his helpful criticism and encouragement I would also express my gratitude. And to many others who have shown enough interest to stimulate me to have the book printed. To the publishers, E. & S. Livingstone, Ltd., and particularly to Mr. Charles Macmillan for the care and interest he has taken with the publication, I am most grateful.

But my greatest debt is, of course, to Shakespeare himself. For all the shortcomings in the comments I accept the responsibility; and I hope I have not misinterpreted or misrepresented Shakespeare too frequently. The study of Shakespeare is very much more than can be achieved in any one man's lifetime. Even the minor aspect of the study of the medical interest in Shakespeare is beyond the scope and ability of any one man in his own life. Indeed, it may be even impossible. But in

v

that hazard of the attempt to understand and explain lies the spur. The achievement can be left to the assessment of the critics. Enough for me that in the leisure of my medical life, I have been more than amply rewarded by my absorption in the interest in the subject. And so, conscious of its deficiences and shortcomings, I offer this contribution to the understanding of Shakespeare's genius to my medical colleagues and, I hope, to some of my literary friends for their consideration, reminding them of what Hazlett said,

'If we wish to know the insignificance of human learning, we may read his commentators'.

R. R. SIMPSON.

Hull, 1959.

CONTENTS

Chapter One

INTRODUCTION

If we wish to know the force of human genius, we should read Shakespeare. If we wish to know the insignificance of human learning, we may read his commentators.

Hazlitt.

SOME justification is needed for adding a new volume to the enormous bibliography of Shakespearian commentary; and at the outset I want to enter my plea in mitigation. E. K. Chambers in an extensive bibliography of authoritative books on Shakespeare—a list comprising at least 450 volumes—records only one which deals with the medical aspects of Shakespeare's writings. That book was written by Dr. John Bucknill and was published in 1860. It was a commentary on the medical aspects of the individual plays, in the light of the medical knowledge of a century ago. In 1906 a small book, written by a general practitioner in Ayrshire, Dr. Moyes, was published posthumously by his medical colleagues. This was a dictionary type of book of the medical references in the plays, but it was by no means complete. Since then, probably the most outstanding paper on the topic is that by Sir St. Clair Thomson, given as the Annual Oration to the London Medical Society in 1916. The material for this paper, however, was taken largely from Bucknill's book of 1860. There have been, of course, numerous papers on certain medical aspects of the plays, but these papers are scattered throughout the medical journals of the world, and mostly they deal with specialised subjects. Frequently, too— too frequently, indeed!—they copy from previously published papers simple errors of fact, of judgment, actual mistakes, and, of course, the inevitable conjectures.

I hope my medical colleagues will find something to interest them, for the study was undertaken primarily from the medical point of view; but I dare to hope, too, that my literary friends will find the medical approach not without interest to them, though the absence of any 'theme' may disappoint. Briefly, the objects of the study were to record the medical references in the plays and poems, to assess Shakespeare's knowledge of the medicine of his day, to consider the uses to which he put it, and to discuss some of the possible sources of his medical knowledge. To illustrate the interest of a medical approach to the study of the plays, a chapter has been devoted to the medical aspects of one play, *Romeo and Juliet*; another chapter to the medical study of one character, Sir John Falstaff; and a further chapter to some of the medical problems raised in the Tragedies.

It is rarely appreciated how often Shakespeare uses a medical image to illustrate a point, or a medical situation at a moment of dramatic intensity. Some impression of the amount of material involved in a study of this kind may be given by the fact that in the 37 plays and the poems of Shakespeare, there are, according to my reading, over 450 major medical references. They are distributed:

Comedies . . .	116
Histories . . .	132
Tragedies . .	182
Poems . . .	25
	455

An attempt has been made to classify the medical references into various groups, but this is a personal and arbitrary classification and it is not meant to be either comprehensive or complete. At least it is one method of classification, and if it stimulates the production of a better one it will have served its purpose. These references can be grouped into about

20 sections, and, if in these are included the minor references, there are just over 700 items to be classified. For my own information I have arranged Shakespeare's medical references in the following way:

MEDICAL REFERENCES IN SHAKESPEARE

Subject	No. of References
1. Medical Aphorisms	50
2. Medical Metaphors and Similes . .	130
3. Medical Folk-lore and Sayings . .	50
4. Anatomy and Physiology . . .	26
5. Clinical Descriptions	80
6. Woman and Marriage . . .	48
7. Pregnancy and Diseases of Women .	28
8. Nursing, Nurses and Midwives . .	12
9. Doctors, Apothecaries and Quacks .	32
10. Drugs and Poisons	25
11. Death, Burial Alive and Suicide . .	31
12. Psychology and Dreams . . .	49
13. Neurosis and Insanity . . .	19
14. Sleep	13
15. Children	17
16. Old Age	18
17. Public Health and Epidemics . .	25
18. The Treatment of Wounds . .	34
19. Diseases of the Ear, Nose and Throat .	42
20. Eyes	25
TOTAL . .	712

That total of 712 items for classification and consideration may cause some surprise; nevertheless it is probably a conservative estimate of the amount of material involved in any study of Shakespeare's medical knowledge and the uses to which he put it.

As an illustration of how the medical references can be classified, consider this passage from *Romeo and Juliet*:

Benvolio. Tut, man, one fire burns out another's burning,
One pain is less'ned by another's anguish;
Turn giddy, and be holp by backward turning;
One desperate grief cures with another's languish.
Take thou some new infection to thy eye,
And the rank poison of the old will die.

Romeo. Your plantain leaf is excellent for that.

Benvolio. For what, I pray thee?

Romeo. For your broken shin.

Benvolio. Why, Romeo, art thou mad?

Romeo. Not mad, but bound more than a
madman is;
Shut up in prison, kept without my food,
Whipt and tormented.

R. & J., I, 2, 45-56.

Benvolio finds four variations of his original image; each variation is a medical aphorism; they are also medical metaphors; and they are probably medical folk-lore sayings of Shakespeare's day. One of the aphorisms—'Turn giddy, and be holp by backward turning'—is an acute clinical observation on the physiology of the ear. Then there is a reference to the manner of treating eye conditions; and counter-irritation in the treatment of certain eye diseases is still sometimes used to-day. There follows what we know now was a method of treating wounds or ulcers in Elizabethan times, i.e. the use of the plantain leaf. Finally, there is the reference to the treatment of a madman in those days, and, as we know from other sources, it is an accurate description of what in fact did happen. So that in this short passage there are medical references which can be classified into 7 of the sections already listed.

Some repetition of certain references in more than one section is unavoidable. As an example, consider one reference which might be regarded as Shakespeare's epitome of all that

has ever been written about Reflex Action and the Conditioned
Reflexes. It is done in four words:

> Mine eyes smell onions.
> *All's W.*, V, 3, 314.

That must be included in the section on Physiology. But it is
also a medical aphorism, and probably a medical folk-lore
saying of the time. It must be included, too, in the section
on the Nose, and also the section on the Eyes. But it is a gem
that never palls, however often it is noted.

On the advice of Professor Peter Alexander, some attempt
has been made at a comparison of the medical knowledge
shown in the plays of Shakespeare's contemporaries. The scope
of such a comparison in a study of this type must naturally be
limited. There was no particular motive or scheme in the
selection of the following contemporary plays, but they were
thought to be fairly representative:

1. *Tamburlaine the Great* (2nd part)   Christopher Marlowe.
2. *Doctor Faustus* .   .   .   .   Christopher Marlowe.
3. *Edward the Second*   .   .   Christopher Marlowe.
4. *The Alchemist* .   .   .   Ben Jonson.
5. *Volpone:* or, *The Fox*   .   Ben Jonson.
6. *The Shoemaker's Holiday*   .   Thomas Dekker.
7. *The White Devil*   .   .   John Webster.
8. *The Duchess of Malfi*   .   John Webster.
9. *The Knight of the Burning Pestle* .   Beaumont and Fletcher.
10. *Philaster*   .   .   .   Beaumont and Fletcher.
11. *A New Way to Pay Old Debts*   Philip Massinger.

The medical references found in these plays were recorded
and classified in the same sections as Shakespeare's, so that a
ready comparison and evaluation could be made on comparable themes.

Not all the sections referred to in the classification are
included as chapters. Only those which appeared to have
some appeal to the general as well as the medical reader have

been retained. An appendix contains the line references of all the medical references in the plays and poems. All these line references are to the Tudor Edition of *William Shakespeare— the complete Works*, edited by Peter Alexander. (Collins, 1951).

Most of the material in the book was prepared originally for lectures to various medical societies. Some new material will be found in the chapter on 'Shakespeare and the influence of his son-in-law, Mr. John Hall, Physician'. The conclusions reached after discussing this controversial subject may perhaps be thought somewhat rash, if not bold, for a non-literary medical, but on the evidence presented they were thought to be worth recording.

SHAKESPEARE'S KNOWLEDGE OF
ELIZABETHAN MEDICINE

And if we cannot deny but that God hath given virtues to springs and fountains, to cold earth, to plants and stones, minerals, and to the excremental parts of the basest living creatures, why should we rob the beautiful stars of their working powers? For seeing they are many in number, and of eminent beauty and magnitude, we may not think that in the Treasury of His wisdom, who is infinite, there can be wanting (even for every star) a peculiar virtue and operation, as every herb, plant, fruit, and flower adorning the face of the earth hath the like. For as these were not created to beautify the earth alone, and to cover and shadow her dusty face, but otherwise for the use of man and beast, to feed them and cure them; so were not those uncountable glorious bodies set in the firmament to no other end than to adorn it, but for instruments and organs of His divine providence, so far as it hath pleased His just will to determine.

Sir Walter Raleigh, *The History of the World*, p. 12.

Some information as to the subjects taught in the different departments of study may be derived from the Elizabethan Statutes of 1570. The duties of the University lecturers are there described in terms almost identical with those of the Edwardian Statutes of 1549. . . . The text-books of the lectures in Medicine were to be Hippocrates or Galen.

Sir John Edwin Sands, *Shakespeare's England*, Vol. I, Ch. 8.

Writers of this period, and not merely the most famous, reveal an astonishing versatility and range of knowledge. Versatility was, of course, an accepted social ideal, but what made possible the varied intellectual activities of Raleigh, Bacon, Selden, Burton, Browne, Sir Kenelm Digby, and many others was the relative compactness of their world of knowledge; politics, law, history, philosophy, poetry, and science could all be touched. But breadth of learning was matched by breadth of experience; most writers were not solely men of letters but had careers in the political, academic, or clerical worlds.

The concentration of cultivated society followed from the overwhelming and growing predominance of London. No other English town approached its population of approximately 300,000, and its increase was not materially checked by plague.

Marjorie Cox, *The Background to English Literature*
(Pelican Book).

Chapter Two

SHAKESPEARE'S KNOWLEDGE OF ELIZABETHAN MEDICINE

Whether Shakespeare was, in fact, acquainted with the literature of contemporary Elizabethan medicine is a question which will probably never be established; but that he was aware of the current medical thought there can be little doubt. To understand and appreciate the medical references found in the plays and poems, some knowledge of the medical thought and writing of the period is essential. In this essay the subject is considered in a general way before going on to the more detailed collection of medical references in subsequent chapters. [1]

The number of medical references to be found throughout the plays is no indication that Shakespeare had any training in medicine. 'In the olden time,' says Bucknill, 'a man might be an admiral, and a general, and a statesman, and a country gentleman, and somewhat of a lawyer, doctor, and divine into the bargain; and this universality of education stamped itself upon the works of the old authors; upon those of Montaigne, for instance; and, above all, upon those of Shakespeare. Hence arises the easy possibility of misjudging the calling of an old writer, from the professional knowledge indicated in his works. There is more of medicine than of law in Bacon's *Essays* and *Advancement of Learning*, and nearly as much of law as of medicine in Rabelais; yet the former was a practising lawyer and a judge; while the latter was a practising physician, and a medical as well as a general author, who, in addition to his immortal biography of Pantagruel

---

[1] Some of the material here discussed is to be found in *Shakespeare's Medical Knowledge*, by John Bucknill, 1860.

9

and Panurge, translated the aphorisms of Hippocrates and some of Galen's works. There is, perhaps, no author who so profusely employs technical terms as Rabelais, and this not only in medicine and in law, but in maritime and other professional business; so that this readiness of one author to use the terms of art proper to several callings, greatly decreases the value of such word-signs, as an indication of the calling of the author himself.'

Bucknill goes on to consider the evidence in the plays of 'the professional habit of mind' and claims that no one has so accurately represented this characteristic as Shakespeare. He cites 'the formalism of the lawyer in Escalius, the self-possession of the doctor in Cordelia's physician, the pedantic strategist in Fluellen, and many other forms of professional characterisation', as evidence of Shakespeare's recognition of 'the sidelong growth of the mind which special education impresses.'

Archbishop Whately in his Rhetoric discusses the intellectual and moral influences of the professions. He indicates the mental peculiarities incidental to the studies of law and medicine and he imputes to the medical profession a tendency to infidelity, and even to atheism, as its most important and prevailing bias, witness the proverb, 'Ubi tres medici duo athei'. This imputation is accepted by Sir Thomas Browne, who, in Religio Medici, nevertheless, in part rebuttal, asserts that 'though in point of devotion and piety, physicians do meet with common obloquy; yet, in the Roman Calendar, we find no less than twenty-nine saints and martyrs of that profession'. Bucknill, after discussing Whately's points, concludes that Shakespeare shows no professional warp of mind. If he had been, indeed, 'in professional harness, it would seem most probable that he had not strained in one direction for seven years, since he could scarcely have done so without contracting some distortion, which would have injured the beautiful symmetry of his powers'. And writing now, almost a century after Bucknill, and having re-examined all the medical evidence in the plays, I can only repeat Bucknill's conclusions. The lost years in Shakespeare's life certainly were not spent in the study of medicine.

When Shakespeare wrote, Medicine, as a science, was not yet even in its infancy. It would be as unfair, therefore, to compare his medical knowledge with that of the present day as it would be to compare Bacon's own chemical absurdities in his *Natural History of the Form of Hot Things* with the scientific enlightenment of Faraday, or, in our own day, of Einstein. In attempting an opinion of the degree in which an old author was acquainted with an old subject, it is evident that the operation of time, which, said Shakespeare,

> doth blot old books, and alter their contents,

must be carefully borne in mind. In his preface to the *Works of Harvey*, Willis makes this same point:

> The interpretation which successive generations of men give to a passage in a writer some century or two old, is very apt to be in consonance with the state of knowledge at that time, in harmony with the prevailing ideas of the day; and, doubtless, often differs signally from the meaning that was in the mind of the man who composed it. The world saw nothing of the circulation of the blood in Servetus, Columbus, Cæsalpinus, or Shakespeare, until after William Harvey had taught and written.

To fit Shakespeare's medicine into its true perspective and its proper background, it is necessary to sketch briefly the state of medicine in the sixteenth and seventeenth centuries. References to the various histories of medicine of about that period are disappointing. Le Clerc's 'History of Physick,' made English by Drs. Drake and Baden, 1699, is monopolised by dissertations on the medicine of the Greeks and the Arabians. The first work which really tackled the subject is Sprengel's *Geschichlite der Artzneikunde*. Hamilton's *History of Medicine* has the advantage of having been written after Sprengel's.

All these works describe successive improvements and the progress of knowledge, but they do not deal with the state of knowledge at any particular time. They do not describe the degree of ignorance as well as that of knowledge, and, with slight exceptions, they do not indicate the social state and position of the men who practised the art while they began to study what there was of the science of medicine. There is no history of medicine which can be referred to with any probability of discovering whether Shakespeare repeated the professional opinion of his day when he asserts—

> the sovereignest thing on earth
> Was parmaceti for an inward bruise.
> 1 *Hen. IV*, I, 3, 58.

But there are two medical writers who in the seventeenth century were still advocating 'parmaceti for an inward bruise'. Woodall affirms this special virtue, almost in the words of Shakespeare:

> Sperma Ceti, or Spuma Maris, or the spawne of the whale, is sowre in taste, spongie and white in shew, unsavoury in smell, and weighty, having a sharp quality, it is of a colde faculty, clenseth and digesteth, and is sometimes used of women to cleare the skin from spots and morphew (ringworm), and it is good also against bruises inwardly, taken with the former, namely Mummia, and also outwardly warme, to annoynt the parts contused therewith, and a Paracelsus emplaster, or of Pix Græcum, put thereon. [1]

And as late as 1693, we find Salmon, [2] writing of parmaceti that 'it is said to be anodyne, and some physicians affirm that it resolves. coagulated blood,' hence the indication for its use in bruises. Probably it was as effective as the modern raw beef-steak for a black-eye!

[1] *The Surgion's Mate*, p. 109, 1617, by John Woodall.
[2] Salmon, *Seplasium, or Druggist Shop opened*

To compare Shakespeare's medicine with the medical thought of his day, the original medical writers of the time must be consulted. This task is amply rewarding for it establishes the fact that Shakespeare's knowledge of medicine corresponded closely to that prevailing at his time among its professors, and that he had authority even for his trivialities and apparent absurdities. Two apparent absurdities may be mentioned here.

> *Don Pedro.*   What! sigh for the toothache?
> *Leonato.*   Where is but a humour or a worm.
> > *Much Ado*, III, 2, 23-24.

That toothache was caused by a 'humour or a worm' was the opinion expressed by John of Gatisden, one of our oldest medical writers (circa 1320) [1]   Fuller [2] records of John of Gatisden that 'lately his works have been printed in Italy in a folio, no small honour, seeing that in physick the Italians account all tramontain doctours but apothecaries in comparison of themselves'. Even in Fuller's time—1650—therefore, the works of John of Gatisden were by no means out of date; and the edition to which Fuller refers was published in 1595, that is, during Shakespeare's writing life.

> Not half so big as a round little worm
> Prick'd from the lazy finger of a maid.
> > *R. & J.*, I, 4, 65-66.

A contemporary reference to this is found in John Bannister's *A Compendious Chyrurgerie*, p. 465, published in 1585.

> We commonly call them worms, which many women, sitting in the sunne shine, can cunningly picke out with nedles, and are most common in the handes.

Bannister was an eminent surgeon of the period.

[1] John of Gatisden, *Rosa Anglica*, liber secundus, De Febribus, p. 923. Edit. 1595—*De Corriosone Dentium.*
[2] Fuller, *Worthies of England.*

For a picture of the background of Shakespearian medicine, some knowledge of the state of the medical profession and of their place in the social life of the community is needed [1] Here, I want to continue the consideration of Shakespeare's medical references and to comment on some of the contemporary medical thought and ideas on which these references were founded.

> *Sir Toby.* Does not our lives consist of the four elements?
>> *T. N.*, II, 3, 9.

It was the accepted medical thought of Shakespeare's time that our bodies consisted of the four elements—fire, air, earth and water. The hypothetical pathology based on this conception, propounded by Plato, was that all diseases arose from the derangement in the due proportion of these elements in the body. He maintained that if the element of fire was in excess, continual fever was the result; if air predominated, quotidians; if water, tertians, and if earth, quartans were the result. [2] Hippocrates elaborated the hypothesis. He 'expressed them not by the names of the substances, but by proper qualities, saying hot, cold, moist, and drie, because some one of these qualities is inherent in every element—thus fire, hot and drie; aire, moist and hot; water, cold and moist; earth, cold and drie.' (Ambroise Paré). Substantially, these were the views adopted by Galen, and, because of his authority, they were accepted implicitly by his adherents. They were accepted, too, by the laity, as, for example in *The Arcadia* of Sir Philip Sydney:

> O elements, by whose (men say) contention
> Our bodies be in living lower maintained,
> Was this man's death the fruit of your dissension?
> O physic's power, which (some say) hath restrained
> Approach of death, alas, thou helpest meagrely,

[1] See introduction to Chap. on *Doctors, Apothecaries and Quacks.*
[2] Le Clerc's *History of Medicine.*

When once one is for Atropos distrained.
Great be physicians' brags, but aide is beggarly,
When rooted moisture failes, or groweth drie,
They leave off all, and say, death comes too eagerly.
They are but words therefore that men doe buy
Of any, since god Esculapius ceased.

Shakespeare refers again to the four elements in Sonnets 44 and 45.

Corresponding to the four elements were the four humours —black bile, blood, bile, phlegm. According as one or other predominated in a man's system so his temperament was choleric or phlegmatic or melancholy, and his complexion in keeping.

Some of the views of Hippocrates were part of the current medical beliefs of Shakespeare's day but there is no direct evidence that, when Shakespeare expressed these Hippocratic views, he was knowingly propounding them. All that can be said is that he was expressing contemporary medical thought. The examples to which I refer can, in three instances, be illustrated from the aphorisms of Hippocrates. The first is referred to as Hippocratic by a medical author writing shortly before Shakespeare.

Say, can you fast? Your stomachs are too young.
And abstinence engenders maladies.

L. L. L., IV, 3, 290-291.

Sir Thomas Elyot[1] writes:

Hipocrates saythe, old menne maye susteyne fastynge easyly, nexte unto theym, menne of myddeil age, yonge menne maye wars beare it, chylderne warst of all, specially they that be lustye, not withstandynge Galene corrected Hipocrates, sayenge, that he shulde have excepted menne very olde, who, as experyence declareth, muste eate often and lyttle.

[1] Sir Thomas Elyot, The Castell of Helthe, p. 55, 1541.

The three examples of Shakespeare's expression of the aphorisms of Hippocrates are:

> *Leonta.*   Being that I flow in grief
> The smallest twine may lead me.
>
>   *Friar.* 'Tis well consented. Presently away;
> For to strange sores strangely they strain the cure.
>
> Much Ado, IV, 1, 249-252.

The sixth aphorism of Hippocrates reads: 'For extreme diseases, extreme methods of cure as to restriction are most suitable'.

> *Prince Henry.* O vanity of sickness! Fierce extremes
> In their continuance will not feel themselves.
> Death, having prey'd upon the outward parts,
> Leaves them insensible, and his siege is now
> Against the mind, the which he pricks and wounds
> With many legions of strange fantasies,
> Which, in their throng and press to that last hold,
> Confound themselves. 'Tis strange that death should sing.
>
> King John, V, 7, 13-20.

Hippocrates noted this phenomenon in the sixth aphorism, sec. 2:

> Persons who have a painful affection of any part of the body, and are in a great measure insensible of pain, are disordered in intellect.

> *Richard.* Wrath-kindled gentlemen, be rul'd by me;
> Let's purge this choler without letting blood—
> This we prescribe, though no physician;
> Deep malice makes too deep incision.
> Forget, forgive; conclude and be agreed:
> Our doctors say this is no month to bleed.
>
> R. II, I, 1, 152-157.

The forty-seventh aphorism, sec. 6, of Hippocrates reads:

> Persons who are benefited by venesection or purging should be bled or purged in the spring.

Sir Thomas Elyot[1] expresses the same opinion—a view which persisted until Shakespeare's time:

> Concernynge lettynge of bloudde, these thynges
> folowynge, wolde be had in contynuall remembraunce,
> and be afore thought on.—The tyme of the yere
> must be speciallye marked. For in the begynnynge
> of the sprynge tyme, it is beste lettynge of
> bloudde, as Oribasius saythe, and so doth continue,
> after the opinyon of Arnolde, unto the eyght calendes
> of June. Ætius affirmeth, that in wynter, or in a
> colde countrey, or where the persone is of a very
> colde nature, the veynes shuld not be opened.

So much for the vague generalities of medieval speculation. To come to the more specific type of Elizabethan ideas in medicine, we can consider their conception of the function of the heart, and how far Shakespeare accepted these ideas. The knowledge we have of Shakespeare's view of the function of the heart and the arteries and the veins is based on four main references.

> *Berowne.*   Why, universal plodding poisons up
> The nimble spirits in the arteries,
> As motion and long-during action tires
> The sinewy vigour of the traveller.
> > *L. L. L.*, lv, 3, 301-304.

> *Hamlet.*   My fate cries out,
> And makes each petty arture in this body
> As hardy as the Nemean lion's nerve.
> > *Ham.*, L, 5, 81-83.

'The nimble spirits in the arteries' expresses accurately the medical theory which prevailed before Harvey, and which held that the arteries were not the channels of the blood, but of the vital spirits. The arteries were supposed to contain air, because they were found empty of blood after death. The trachea, or windpipe, was called 'arteria aspersa' from the

[1] Sir Thomas Elyot, *The Castell of Helthe*, p. 55, 1541.

roughness of its rings. Hamlet's 'each petty arture' refers to this same theory, in which the arteries become inflated in excitement.

Falstaff's dissertation on the two-fold operation of a 'good sherris-sack' adds considerably to our knowledge of what Shakespeare probably believed, or, at least, what his contemporary medical theorists believed.

> It ascends me into the brain; dries me there
> all the foolish and dull and crudy vapours
> which environ it
>
> the warming of the blood; which before, cold
> and settled, left the liver white and pale
>
> makes it course from the inwards to the
> parts extreme
>
> the vital commoners and inland petty spirits
> muster me all to their captain, the heart

Up to the time of Harvey it was believed that the veins were the only blood-vessels and that they originated in the liver. This belief had been maintained ever since it was first propounded by Hippocrates; indeed, it had become an article of medical faith. The origin of the theory appears to have been the statement by Hippocrates in his *Book of Ailments*:

> The root of the veins is the liver, and the
> root of the arteries is the heart; and from
> them blood and spirits are carried to all
> parts, and heat passes with the same.

The heart—the generator of heat and the vital spirits—was merely the cistern of the blood, which was propelled on inspiration and returned on expiration. The flow of blood to any particular part of the body was determined by certain inherent excitations of that part, or specially set up there.

The great anatomists, Eustachius and Fallopius, both accepted this view of the origin of the veins. [1]

> Brutus.   You are my true and honourable
> wife,
> As dear to me as are the ruddy drops
> That visit my sad heart.
>
> J. C., II, 1, 288-290.

This was at one time considered to be a distinct reference to the circulation of the blood, described by William Harvey in 1616, the year of Shakespeare's death. It was argued then that either the play, *Julius Caesar*, was not written as early as 1603 (the date under discussion in the argument here referred to) or that Shakespeare had been acquainted with Harvey and had learned from him about the circulation of the blood. But there is no evidence that Shakespeare knew Harvey. Harvey's first ideas on the subject were not made public until the week before Shakespeare's death, when he delivered his first course of Lumleian lectures. His book was not published until 1628, twelve years after Shakespeare's death. Shakespeare could not have known Harvey in 1603 for at that time Harvey was abroad, and, whatever ideas he may have had about the discovery of the valves in the veins, there is no evidence in any of Harvey's writings to shew that he had, at that date, any new ideas about the circulation of the blood. There is no doubt that Shakespeare was still referring in this play to the Galenical doctrine, universally prevalent before Harvey's discovery, that, although the right side of the heart was visited by the blood, the function of the heart and its vessels, the arteries, was the distribution of the vital spirits—'the nimble spirits in the arteries'. Certainly Shakespeare believed in the flow of the blood—'the rivers of your blood' which went 'even to the court, the heart'; but he accepted that it was the

[1] Bucknill thinks that the clearest and most succinct account of the opinions of the sixteenth century on physiology was written by Rabelais in *The History of Gargantua and Pantagruel*, Book 3, Ch. 3.

liver, and not the heart, which was the cause of the flow. There is, in my reading, no evidence to be found in Shakespeare of any knowledge of the circulation of the blood.

An example of how an Elizabethan medical belief can persist into comparatively recent times is found in Bucknill's comment on the cause of jaundice.

> *Gratiano.* With mirth and laughter let old
> wrinkles come;
> And let my liver rather heat with wine
> Than my heart cool with mortifying groans.
> Why should a man whose blood is warm within
> Sit like his grandsire cut in alabaster,
> Sleep when he wakes, and creep into the jaundice
> By being peevish?
>
> *M. of V.,* I, 1, 80-86.

It will surprise modern medical men, no doubt, to find that Bucknill, writing as recently as 1860, asserts dogmatically that in this passage 'the intimate connexion between mind and body is sketched with exact physiological truth. Perhaps the most curious and undoubted instance of the mind's influence in the production of bodily disease is jaundice caused by depressing emotion. It is not always "crept" into, since bad news has frequently been known to cause jaundice in a few hours. In Dr. Copland's great and learned *Dictionary of Medicine*, it is stated that "The most common exciting causes of jaundice are the more violent mental emotions", and in the list of these emotions which he adds, he specially includes "peevishness". In Dr. Watson's *Lectures on Physic*, that able physician states that among the causes of jaundice "the 'pathemata mentis' play their assigned part; fits of anger and fear and alarm have been presently followed by jaundice".' Such a commentary should be a warning to any medical writer against the dangerous assumption of infallibility when expounding the shifting tides of medical opinion. To-day, of the many accepted causes of jaundice, neither peevishness nor any of the 'pathemata mentis' would find a place.

Shakespeare was well aware of the ancient practice of recognising diseases by the inspection of the patient's urine. He refers to it on at least three occasions.

1. *Maria.* Pray God, he be not bewitched!

   Fabian. Carry his water to the wise woman.

                   Twelfth Night, III, 4, 96-97.

2.   *Speed.* . . . you are so without these follies that these follies are within you, and shine through you like the water in an urinal, that not an eye that sees you but is a physician to comment on your malady.

              Two Gentlemen of Verona, II, 1, 32-36.

3.   *Macbeth.* If thou couldst, doctor, cast
The water of my land, find her disease,
And purge it to a sound and pristine health,
I would applaud thee to the very echo,
That should applaud again. . . .
What rhubarb, senna, or what purgative drug,
Would scour these English hence?

              Macbeth, V, 3, 50-56.

It was a very old custom; indeed, it was said to have arisen, like the origin of the Barber-Surgeons, from the prohibition imposed on the clergy of practising medicine by visiting the patient. Priests and monks were forbidden to visit patients in their homes, so the idea arose of diagnosing disease by having the patient's urine brought to them, and then suggesting treatment.

The earliest English physician to write on the subject was Richardus Anglicus (circa 1230). He left two works—*A Tractate of Urines* and *On the Rules of Urines*. But the uncertainty and pretentiousness of medical opinion founded on this form of charlatanism was recognized by the beginning of the sixteenth century. In 1550, an Oxford physician, Robert Recorde, wrote *Of the Judgments of Urine*; and of him, Fuller, in his *Worthies of England*, comments—'his judicious rules have reduced that harlot to honesty, and in a great measure fixed the uncertainty thereof'. This form of quackery was still, however, much in vogue in Shakespeare's day, but the College of Physicians wrote bitterly against it. Linacre was [1]

> so concerned at the ridiculous humour of nurses and other women, who upon every ailment, both great and small, were too ready to carry about the patient's urine, expecting they should be told all things from the mere speculation of it, would often advise them in ridicule, to bring the patient's shoe instead of the urine, and he would prophesie full as well over that. Nay, further, there were a sort of knaves in his days, who, considering how well the vulgar would relish anything of novelty, though never so absurd, would undertake to make discoveries of diseases from the smell of the patient's shoe, as solemnly and seriously as others from the urine.

There was an old statute of the College of Physicians which denounced water-casting as belonging to tricksters and impostors, and members of the College were forbidden to give advice upon the mere inspection of the urine without also seeing the patient. The statute runs [2] :

> Idcirco volumus et Statuimus, ut nullus sive Collega sive Candidatus sive permissus ad praxin quicquid de suo consilio impertiat, istiusmodi veteratoriis Impostoribus super urinarum tantummodo inspectiones, nisi in reliquâ totâ illâ Curâ adhibeatur ut Medicus in consilium, et durante illo morbo de tempore in tempus novas deinceps medicinas easque Latine ad honestum aliquem Apothecarium praescripserit, prout morbi illius natura et aliqua inde nata occasio quotidie postulaverit, etc.

Forestus in his *Medical Politics*, writing on this topic, insists that the signs of the urine must be studied in conjunction

---

[1] Dr. Harris, *Pharmacologica Anti-Empirica*, 1683.

[2] *De Chirurgorum Imposturis evitandis*, Statuta vetera, c. 1601. The original MS. is in the Bodleian Library, Oxford. I am indebted to L. M. Payne, F.L.A., Assistant Librarian, Royal College of Phsyicians, for this information.

with those of the pulse, 'Urinae fraudes aperit discretio pulsus.'
He goes on to explain how various attempted frauds are to be
detected, 'how wine or any other liquor, or the urine of cattle'
are to be recognised when used to deceive the water-caster.
The need for care is illustrated by what was regarded at that
time as a 'merry story'.

A certain maid did carry her mistress's urine to a physician,
and having by chance spilled it, not knowing what to doe, she
catched the urine of a cow, which at that time by good hap
staled, and carried it to the physician: he gave answer that the
patient did eat too many salletts.

Another 'droll' story is recorded by Forestus:

A noble lady wishing to deceive a physician, celebrated for
his skill in water-casting, took to him the urine of a sick farmer;
the physician, suspecting the deceit from the lady's arch look,
and observing that the jug was stoppered with a herb which
grew in a certain spot, said, while he poured the urine from the
poculum to the matula, This belongs to some rustic not of this
town but of the country through such a gate; and thus astonishing
his visitor, he easily got from her an account of the disease and
obtained her great admiration of his skill.

Among Shakespeare's contemporary dramatists, only
Webster refers to water-casting, and he shares the views of the
College.

> Bosola.   Doth he study physiognomy?
> There's no more credit to be given to th' face
> Than to a sick man's urine, which some call
> The physician's whore because she cozens him.
> > *The Duchess of Malfi*, I, 1, 255-258.

Probably Marlowe's physician in Tamburlaine presents for
us the best epitome of Elizabethan medicine:

> *Physician.*   Pleaseth your majesty to drink this
>   potion,
> Which will abate the fury of your fit,
> And cause some milder spirits govern you.

Tamburlaine. Tell me what think you of my
sickness now?

Physician. I view'd your urine, and the hypostasis,
Thick and obscure, doth make your danger great:
Your veins are full of accidental heat,
Whereby the moisture of your blood is dried:
The humidum and calor, which some hold
Is not a parcel of the elements,
But of a substance more divine and pure,
Is almost clean extinguished and spent;
Which, being the cause of life, imports your death:
Besides, my lord, this day is critical,
Dangerous to those whose crisis is as yours:
Your artiers, which along the veins convey
The lively spirits which the heart engenders,
Are parch'd and void of spirits, that the soul,
Wanting those organons by which it moves,
Cannot endure, by argument of art.
Yet, if your majesty may escape this day,
No doubt but you shall soon recover all.

Tamburlaine. Then will I comfort all my vital parts,
And live, in spite of death, above a day.

Tamburlaine (2nd pt.), V, 3.

Chapter Three

THE MEDICAL ASPECTS OF 'ROMEO AND JULIET'

The rapid, alert reading of one of the great plays brings us nearer to the heart of Shakespeare than all the faithful and laudable business of the antiquary and the commentator.

Sir Walter Raleigh, *Shakespeare*, p. 7.

BEFORE going on to the more general study of the Medicine of Shakespeare, it may help if we consider the medical aspects of one of his plays in a little detail. There are several advantages in choosing *Romeo and Juliet* as an example. To begin with, it is one of the general favourites, and, therefore, well known and widely read. It was written not later than 1595, and so we can be sure that at that time Shakespeare was not influenced in his medical references by either Dr. William Harvey or by his own medical son-in-law, John Hall [1]. Neither of these distinguished doctors come into the story of Shakespeare's life until after the turn of the century. While there is no doctor in the play, Friar Lawrence, as a priest-physician, can be considered to represent the best medical tradition of the day. In addition, of course, there is a nurse, an apothecary, and the Public Health Authority; and, although he takes no part in the play, a surgeon is mentioned. But the main advantage is that, because of the number of references of medical interest in it, it may be considered 'the medical play'. At least one medical reference in the play can be put into each of the twenty classified sections mentioned in the Introduction; and the sum total of the medical references, major and minor, amounts to no less than 54.

It will serve our purpose best if we consider the medical aspects of the play in four ways. First, we can note the medical

[1] This may be amplified by referring to the Chap. on 'Shakespeare and the influence of his son-in-law, Mr. John Hall, Physician.'

references as they arise in the unfolding of the drama; next,
we can examine the intrinsic value of each medical reference
or incident; we can then assess the medical characters in the
play; and, finally, we can discuss any medical problems found
in it.

The first medical reference to be noted is in I, 1, 200-201,
the medical image used by Romeo:

> Bid a sick man in sadness make his will.
> Ah, word ill urg'd to one that is so ill!

In his protest at Rosaline's lack of response to his wooing,
I , 1, 213-218, Romeo repeats the theme of the opening
Sonnets (1-3):

> *Romeo.*   O, she is rich in beauty; only poor
> That, when she dies, with beauty dies her store.
> *Benvolio.*   Then she hath sworn that she will still
> live chaste?
> *Romeo.*   She hath, and in that sparing makes huge
> waste;
> For beauty, starv'd with her severity,
> Cuts beauty off from all posterity.

The first medical aphorism in the play (I, 1, 230-231) is an
impressive and realistic one:

> He that is strucken blind cannot forget
> The precious treasure of his eyesight lost.

In Sc. 2, 8-13, there is the argument between Capulet and
Paris about the correct age for marriage and the first pregnancy. This is taken up again in Sc. 3 by Lady Capulet.

Later in this scene (1, 45-55) there is the discussion—full of
medical references—between Benvolio and Romeo.

The whole of Sc. 3 can be given over to the Nurse, one of the
really great medical characters produced by Shakespeare.
But it should be noted here that though the play is so widely
known, the subject here discussed by the Nurse is rarely

remembered. Lady Capulet's view on the marriageable age has already been noted.

Mercutio's long speech on his dream (Sc. 4) contains many points of medical interest. It should be, indeed, a paradise for the psycho-analysts. The entire speech could be regarded as an old wife's tale—and a country one, too!—straight from Shakespeare's own countryside. There has been some discussion about the identity of the waggoner of Queen Mab, the fairies' midwife:

> a small grey-coated gnat,
> Not half so big as a round little worm,
> Prick'd from the lazy finger of a maid.

Bucknill recalls the comment of John Bannister:

> We commonly call them worms, which many women sitting in the sunne shine, can cunningly pick out with nedles, and are most common in the hands. [1]

Bucknill agrees that Mercutio's 'illustration was in perfect accord with medical opinion', i.e. of Shakespeare's day, but he doubts if the condition referred to could have been due to Scabies (the Itch). He thinks 'acarus scabiei', being more like a lobster, under the microscope, than a worm, could not have been what Shakespeare meant. But Bucknill overlooked the reference to 'a small grey-coated gnat', which is what 'acarus scabiei' does resemble. On the old medical principle that 'common things occur most commonly', I do not doubt that Shakespeare was referring to the common and prevalent skin condition known as Scabies, or the Itch.

In Sc. 5 Capulet, in the heartiness of his welcome, teases to provoke:

> Welcome, gentlemen! Ladies that have their toes
> Unplagu'd with corns will have a bout with you.
> Ah Ha, my mistresses! which of you all
> Will now deny to dance? She that makes dainty,
> She I'll swear hath corns; am I come near ye now?

[1] John Bannister (1585), *A Compendious Chyrurgerie*, p. 465.

We move to Act II, Sc. 2, 1, to find another of Romeo's medical aphorisms:

> He jests at scars that never felt a wound

Medically, there is nothing more in this scene until the very end, where we find the almost hypnotic line:

> Sleep dwell upon thine eyes, peace in thy breast!

In Sc. 3, Friar Lawrence expounds the Elizabethan theory about herbal remedies, and he follows this with a commentary which reveals Shakespeare's great insight and understanding of Sleep.

The next point of interest in this Act comes in Sc. 5 when we return to the Nurse and the revelation of her signs and symptoms. In Sc. 6 we find a favourite medical aphorism of Shakespeare's, the paradox of the sweetness of honey.

In Act III, 2, 53-56, we return to the Nurse and her reaction to the sight of Tybalt's wound and blood.

In Act IV, 1, 91-108, Friar Lawrence instructs Juliet about the drug she is to take and the effects it will have on her. Juliet's doubts and fears about this drug are expressed in Sc. 3, 24-58, and many a patient who has waited for an anaesthetic will appreciate and share sympathetically in Juliet's doubts. In Sc. 5, Capulet's description of Juliet as he finds her must be contrasted with Romeo's later description as she lies on the tomb. There is an interesting medical point here.

In Act V, 1, the appearance of the Apothecary is brief but what a wealth of description is packed into this short scene. Sc. 2 tells why the letter was not delivered, and now we begin to feel that tragedy is inevitable. Shakespeare was familiar with 'the infectious pestilence', and the rules of the city authorities were strict during the Plague. In Sc. 3, the last scene, we can comment on Romeo's description of Juliet as she lies on the tomb, his use of the word 'lightning', and the fact that Juliet uses a dagger to kill herself.

So far we have merely found where the medical interest lies in the various acts and scenes. Now the intrinsic value of some of the medical references or incidents can be examined in a little more detail.

Capulet is reluctant to see his daughter married before she has reached the age of puberty—'She hath not seen the change of fourteen years'—and he would prefer to wait until she is at least sixteen before he thinks her 'ripe to be a bride'. Paris argues that 'younger than she are happy mothers made'; and, indeed, Lady Capulet maintains that she herself 'was your mother much upon the years that you are now a maid'. To add weight to her plea, she tells Juliet that in Verona, ladies of esteem, younger than Juliet, were already mothers. It is possibly true that when the original story of Romeo and Juliet was written girls in Italy were married at puberty, and even earlier. [1] It is certainly true that, if they were not actually married, they were betrothed at about that age in Shakespeare's time. There is no question, however, that medical opinion would support Capulet:

'And too soon marr'd are those so early made.'

The medical aphorisms which come into the discussion between Romeo and Benvolio have already been noted. These aphorisms are also folk-lore sayings and they were probably old saws of the country wise-women and the common sayings of the grandmothers of Shakespeare's day, or any other time. They illustrate how succinctly Shakespeare expresses an idea, and when they embody a medical concept they are invaluable as medical folk-lore. Throughout the play there are at least ten of these medical aphorisms, and they are worth listing here.

[1] See Peter Alexander (1944), *Shakespeare's Life and Art*, p. 114.

1. He that is strucken blind cannot forget
   The precious treasure of his eyesight lost.

2. Younger than she are happy mothers made.
   And too soon marr'd are those so early made.

3. One pain is less'ned by another's anguish.

4. Turn giddy, and be holp by backward turning.

5. Take thou some new infection to thy eye,
   And the rank poison of the old will die.

6. He jests at scars that never felt a wound.

7. Within the infant rind of this weak flower
   Poison hath residence, and medicine power.

8. Care keeps his watch in every old man's eye,
   And where care lodges sleep will never lie;
   But where unbruised youth with unstuff'd brain
   Doth couch his limbs, there golden sleep doth reign.

9.   The sweetest honey
   Is loathsome in his own deliciousness,
   And in the taste confounds the appetite.

10. How oft when men are at the point of death
    Have they been merry! Which their keepers call
    A lightning before death.

Although it is 'lightning' in the Folio, it is accepted, for example, by Onions and by Alexander, to mean 'lightening'. This is the actual sense in which this medical phenomenon is met with in, for instance, 'spes phthisica'. It is meant to convey the exhilaration, or rallying of the spirit which not infrequently does occur before death in patients suffering from prolonged toxic illnesses.

The paradox of the 'sweet-sour' image is used by Shakespeare in several variants, e.g.:

1. For as a surfeit of the sweetest things
   The deepest loathing to the stomach brings.
                                    MND, II, 2, 137-138.

2.   Things sweet to taste prove in digestion sour.

> R. II, I, 3, 236.

3.   So surfeit-taking Tarquin fares this night:
His taste delicious, in digestion souring.

> The Rape of Lucrece, 698-699.

4.   They are as sick that surfeit with too much, as they that
starve with nothing. It is no mean happiness, therefore, to
be seated in the mean: superfluity comes sooner by white
hairs; but competency lives longer.

> M. of V., I, 2, 5-8.

5.   If music be the food of love, play on;
Give me excess of it, that, surfeiting,
The appetite may sicken, and so die.

> T. N., I, 1, 1-3.

The age at which Juliet was weaned and the method of
weaning are of considerable medical interest.   Yet it is surprising how few people who have read the play and even
know it well can recall the actual details.   The Nurse is quite
precise on both points.

> On Lammas Eve at night shall she be fourteen;
> That shall she, marry; I remember it well.
> 'Tis since the earthquake now eleven years;
> And she was wean'd—I never shall forget it—
> Of all the days of the year, upon that day.

Weaning nowadays usually begins about the eighth month
and should be completed by one year at the latest.   An explanation of the Nurse's prolonged breast-feeding may be the
erroneous folk-lore superstition that so long as a mother is
breast-feeding her baby she cannot become pregnant.   The
method of weaning was probably commonly used in country
districts in Shakespeare's time.   Needless to say the method is
not used now.

> For I had then laid wormwood to my dug,
> Sitting in the sun under the dove-house wall;
> My lord and you were then at Mantua.

Nay, I do bear a brain. But, as I said,
When it did taste the wormwood on the nipple
Of my dug, and felt it bitter, pretty fool.
To see it tetchy, and fall out with the dug!

Any discussion of Shakespeare's ideas on the psychology of
Dreams is beyond the scope of this study, but there is ample
material for the psychologist in the Queen Mab speech.
There is, too, some medical interest in the folk-lore of the
speech. Romeo believes dreams can be true.

> *Romeo.*   I dreamt a dream to-night.
> *Mercutio.*   And so did I.
> *Romeo.*   Well, what was yours?
> *Mercutio.*   That dreamers often lie.
> *Romeo.*   In bed asleep, while they do dream
>   things true.

We have to wait until the end of the Queen Mab speech
before we hear Mercutio's opinions of dreams.

> *Mercutio.*   True, I talk of dreams,
> Which are the children of an idle brain,
> Begot of nothing but vain fantasy:
> Which is as thin of substance as the air,
> And more inconstant than the wind, who woos
> Even now the frozen bosom of the north,
> And, being anger'd, puffs away from thence,
> Turning his side to the dew-dropping south.

And if that view of the psychology of dreams does not satisfy
the Freudian psychologists, it does give some comfort to
those of us who relish the poetry of it—the vain fantasy of
an idle brain. Another reference to dreams is an illustration
of Shakespeare's use of ingenious paradoxes. Romeo's dreams
(V. 1, 1-9) reverse the position of the lovers in the plan of the
good Friar.

Romeo.   If I may trust the flattering truth of sleep,
My dreams presage some joyful news at hand.

. . . .

I dreamt my lady came and found me dead—
Strange dream that gives a dead man leave to think!—
And breath'd such life with kisses in my lips,
That I reviv'd, and was an emperor.

There is no certain, agreed cause of the cold blisters which
occasionally plague ladies' lips, and the folk-lore explanation
given was probably accepted by the Elizabethans as it could
be in country districts to-day. Queen Mab's carriage galloped:

O'er ladies' lips, who straight on kisses dream,
Which oft the angry Mab with blisters plagues,
Because their breaths with sweetmeats tainted are.

Friar Lawrence is an example of the medieval priest-
physician. His type disappeared eventually with the foundation
of the College of Physicians by Henry VIII. [1]   His soliloquy
is an exposition of the philosophy of the astrologer-physician's
belief in the herbal medicine of the XVIth century.

The gray-ey'd morn smiles on the frowning night,
Check'ring the eastern clouds with streaks of light;
And fleckel'd darkness like a drunkard reels
From forth day's path and Titan's fiery wheels.
Now, ere the sun advance his burning eye
The day to cheer and night's dank dew to dry,
I must up-fill this osier cage of ours
With baleful weeds and precious-juiced flowers.
The earth that's nature's mother is her tomb;
What is her burying grave, that is her womb.
And from her womb children of divers kind
We sucking on her natural bosom find;
Many for many virtues excellent,
None but for some, and yet all different.
O, mickle is the powerful grace that lies
In plants, herbs, stones, and their true qualities;

[1] See Chap. on 'Shakespeare's Doctors, Apothecaries and Quacks'.

For nought so vile that on the earth doth live
But to the earth some special good doth give;
Nor aught so good but, strain'd from that fair use,
Revolts from true birth, stumbling on abuse:
Virtue itself turns vice, being misapplied,
And vice sometime's by action dignified.
Within the infant rind of this weak flower
Poison hath residence, and medicine power;
For this, being smelt, with that part cheers each part;
Being tasted, slays all senses with the heart.
Two such opposed kings encamp them still
In man as well as herbs—grace and rude will;
And where the worser is predominant,
Full soon the canker death eats up that plant.

The comment on Sleep which follows is one of many which Shakespeare makes on this subject. In a medical sense they are all sound and valuable.

Young son, it argues a distempered head
So soon to bid good morrow to thy bed,
Care keeps his watch in every old man's eye,
And where care lodges sleep will never lie;
But where unbruised youth with unstuff'd brain
Doth couch his limbs, there golden sleep doth reign.

We are not told what the drug was that Friar Lawrence gave to Juliet, nor have we any evidence on which we may make any deduction; and it is quite useless to speculate on this question. It was a 'distilled liquor', the favourite method used by the alchemists in preparing their potent drugs. [1] We have no information from these days to confirm that it was possible to estimate accurately the length of time the drug might act. It is fair to assume that Shakespeare was using a justifiable poetic licence to fit in with his plot; and he knew that his audience would not quibble about such unnecessary details. His accurate clinical description of the profound effect of such a narcotic would doubtless so impress his

[1] See Chap. on 'Shakespeare's Drugs and Poisons'.

audience that their critical sense about such details would be forgotten in the rapidity of the action of the play. But the medical value of Shakespeare's clinical description of the action of a powerful narcotic must be noted.

> Take thou this vial, being then in bed,
> And this distilled liquor drink thou off;
> When presently through all thy veins shall run
> A cold and drowsy humour; for no pulse
> Shall keep his native progress, but surcease;
> No warmth, no breath, shall testify thou livest;
> The roses in thy lips and cheeks shall fade
> To paly ashes, thy eyes' windows fall,
> Like death when he shuts up the day of life;
> Each part, depriv'd of supple government,
> Shall, stiff and stark and cold, appear like death;
> And in this borrow'd likeness of shrunk death
> Thou shalt continue two and forty hours,
> And then awake as from a pleasant sleep.
> Now, when the bridegroom in the morning comes
> To rouse thee from thy bed, there art thou dead.

The Nurse is surely the original of all the garrulous nannies of this world. She is the first of Shakspeare's characters 'to sustain an individual form of speech throughout the play' (Reese). And how well we come to know her! We can imagine her as the blowsey, stumpy woman, well past middle-age, suffering from high blood-pressure, easily and wildly excitable, keeping up an incessant chatter of gossip and reminiscence, which is embellished with the bawdiness usually associated with her type.

> I'll lay fourteen of my teeth—
> And yet, to my teen be it spoken, I have but four.
>   I, 3, 13-14.

> And then my husband—God be with his soul!
> 'A was a merry man—took up the child.
> 'Yea', quoth he 'dost thou fall upon thy face?
> Thou wilt fall backward when thou hast more wit,

Wilt thou not, Jule?' And, by my holidam,
The pretty wretch left crying, and said 'Ay'.
To see, now, how a jest shall come about!
I warrant, an I should live a thousand years,
I never should forget it: 'Wilt thou not, Jule?' quoth he;
And, pretty fool, it stinted, and said 'Ay'.

Lady C.   Enough of this: I pray thee hold thy peace.

Nurse.   Yes, madam. Yet I cannot choose but laugh
To think it should leave crying and say 'Ay'.
And yet, I warrant, it had upon its brow
A bump as big as a young cock'rel's stone—
A perilous knock; and it cried bitterly.
'Yea', quoth my husband 'fall'st upon thy face?
Thou wilt fall backward when thou comest to age;
Wilt thou not, Jule?' It stinted, and said 'Ay'.

I, 3, 40-58.

Were I not thine only nurse,
I would say thou hadst suck'd wisdom from thy teat.

I, 3, 68-69.

No less! Nay, bigger; women grow by men.

I, 3, 96.

Nay, afore God, I am so vex'd that every part about me
quivers.   Scurvy knave!

II, 4, 156-157.

Another aspect of her character—the perverse, tantalising
habit of withholding the essential information till the last
possible moment—is illustrated in II, 5. Juliet has sent the
Nurse to Romeo to find out about the arrangements for the
wedding at Friar Lawrence's cell. The Nurse has been away
three hours, and Juliet had expected her to return in half an
hour. When she does return and sees how desperately anxious
Juliet is for news, she tantalises Juliet—and the audience!—
by her seeming pre-occupation with her own symptoms of
fatigue and distress. It is only at the very end of the scene
that she discloses the instructions which Juliet has been waiting
for so impatiently. This short scene is a masterpiece of feminine

perversity. But the Nurse, dwelling on her symptoms, is a very familiar type to any doctor.

> I am aweary, give me leave a while;
> Fie, how my bones ache! What a jaunce have I had.
>
> . . . .
>
> Jesu, what haste? Can you not stay a while?
> Do you not see that I am out of breath?
>
> . . . .
>
> Lord, how my head aches! What a head have I!
> It beats as it would fall in twenty pieces.
> My back a t'other side—ah, my back, my back!
> Beshrew your heart for sending me about
> To catch my death with jauncing up and down!
>
> . . . .
>
>   O God's dear lady!
> Are you so hot? Marry, come up, I trow;
> Is this the poultice for my aching bones?
> Henceforward, do your messages yourself.
>
> . . . .
>
> I am the drudge, and toil in your delight;
> But you shall bear the burden soon at night.

These same delaying tactics are repeated when she brings Juliet news of Tybalt's death in III, 2, though in this instance Juliet—and the audience!—do show some justifiable impatience with her. In her excitement all she can think of is the sight of the dead Tybalt, and the effect it has on her. She even forgets to mention that it was Tybalt, while Juliet is near frantic assuming that she is talking about Romeo.

> I saw the wound, I saw it with mine eyes—
> God save the mark!—here on his manly breast.
> A piteous corse, a bloody piteous corse;
> Pale, pale as ashes, all bedaub'd in blood,
> All in gore-blood. I swounded at the sight.

To complete the clinical picture of the Nurse, Shakespeare adds the touch of her liking for aqua-vitae. Twice she calls for it.

> Ah, where's my man? Give me some aqua-vitae.
> These griefs, these woes, these sorrows, make me old.
>
> III, 2, 88-89.

> Alas, alas! Help, help! my lady's dead!
> O well-a-day that ever I was born!
> Some aqua-vitae, ho!
>
> IV, 5, 14-16.

Perhaps the midwives of Shakespeare's time really did work better with a stimulant, for he mentions it again in *Twelfth Night*.

> *Maria.*   Nay, but say true; does it work upon him.
> *Sir Toby.*   Like aqua-vitae with a midwife.
>
> II, 5, 175-179

The description of the Apothecary does not tally with the reputation of Elizabethan apothecaries. On the contrary, they were regarded as wealthy men, and they were accused of aping the still wealthier physicians, in their rich velvets and the expensive trappings of their horses. Why, then, has Shakespeare gone so contrary to the generally accepted picture of an apothecary of his time? The answer is simple and would be appreciated by his audience at once. In the first place he is an Italian apothecary, adopted with the story from the Italian: so the audience would have no difficulty in imagining a poor, foreign apothecary. Secondly, the sale of poison in Mantua 'is present death':

> Such mortal drugs I have; but Mantua's law
> Is death to any he that utters them.

A rich apothecary would not be amenable to a bribe, but a poor one would be susceptible to forty ducats; and so the apothecary is made to be foreign, poor and starving:

> I do remember an apothecary,
> And here abouts 'a dwells, which late I noted
> In tatt'red weeds, with overwhelming brows,
> Culling of simples. Meagre were his looks;
> Sharp misery had worn him to the bones.
>
> . . . .

> Art thou so bare and full of wretchedness
> And fearest to die? Famine is in thy cheeks,
> Need and oppression starveth in thy eyes,
> Contempt and beggary hangs upon thy back,
> The world is not thy friend, nor the world's law;
> The world affords no law to make thee rich;
> Then be not poor, but break it and take this.

It is the apothecary's 'poverty but not my will consents', and that would be reason enough to the Elizabethan audience.

As the law was so strict, Shakespeare had to find a way of getting the apothecary to discuss the sale of poison without the presence of any customer in the shop. He finds a very simple solution:

> As I remember, this should be the house.
>   Being holiday, the beggar's shop is shut.
>   What, ho! Apothecary!

But the shop and its contents would be readily recognised by the audience from Shakespeare's description of it.

> And in his needy shop a tortoise hung,
> An alligator stuff'd, and other skins
> Of ill-shap'd fishes; and about his shelves
> A beggarly account of empty boxes,
> Green earthen pots, bladders, and musty seeds,
> Remnants of packthread, and old cakes of roses,
> Were thinly scattered, to make up a show. [1]

Friar John's failure to deliver Friar Lawrence's letter to Romeo makes tragedy inevitable. The reason for the failure would be familiar and natural enough both to Shakespeare and his audience.

> Going to find a barefoot brother out,
> One of our order, to associate me,
> Here in this city visiting the sick,
> And finding him, the searchers of the town,

---

[1] See Chap. on 'Shakespeare's Drugs and Poisons'.

> Suspecting that we both were in a house
> Where the infectious pestilence did reign,
> Seal'd up the doors, and would not let us forth,
> So that my speed to Mantua there was stay'd.

> Who bare my letter, then, to Romeo?

> I could not send it—here it is again—
> Nor get a messenger to bring it thee,
> So fearful were they of infection.

The laws and regulations about houses infected by the plague were strongly worded and strictly enforced. [1]

To the medical mind, the tragedy of the Tomb scene has, in its pathos, an added poignant intensity. The audience is warned by the Friar that the drug will make Juliet appear in 'borrow'd likeness of shrunk death' and that she will continue so for forty-two hours; and so they are amused rather than alarmed by the deception practised on old Capulet when he describes her appearance:

> She's cold;
> Her blood is settled, and her joints are stiff.
> Life and these lips have long been separated.
> Death lies on her like an untimely frost
> Upon the sweetest flower of all the field.

But the lapse of time in the passing of the scenes is long enough for the audience to feel not quite so assured about Juliet's appearance as she lies on the tomb. The awful fear must arise in their minds that she may not after all recover in time. This anxiety is increased by Romeo's description of her, he supposes, as a corpse.

> Death, that hath suck'd the honey of thy breath,
> Hath had no power yet upon thy beauty.
> Thou art not conquer'd; beauty's ensign yet
> Is crimson in thy lips and in thy cheeks,
> And death's pale flag is not advanced there.

[1] For a fuller account of the laws on the Plague, etc., see Chap. on 'Shakespeare on Public Health and Epidemics'.

But, to the medical mind, his own description of her appearance—'beauty's ensign yet is crimson in thy lips and in thy cheeks'— should have told Romeo that death had not sucked the honey of her breath, and that her appearance was in reality the 'borrow'd likeness of shrunk death'. The medical mind must be appalled at so accurate a picture of life being accepted so fatalistically as one of death and tragedy. The pity of it!

Chapter Four

THE MEDICAL HISTORY OF SIR JOHN FALSTAFF

FALSTAFF first appears in Henry IV (part 1): he becomes a really great character in Henry IV (part 2): he does not appear in Henry V but the description of his death is one of the great moments of the play: finally, he is recalled to life —it is said at the pressing request of Queen Elizabeth—for a somewhat inglorious spell in *The Merry Wives of Windsor.* Just as the character of Falstaff grew, developed and matured into the immortal personality and then died, so also can we trace the entire compass of his medical history. Medically, we know him from the time he was born:

> about three of the clock in the afternoon, with a white head and something a round belly,

until his death

> Old, cold, wither'd, and of intolerable entrails.

For the benefit of non-medical readers, perhaps it would be wise to make a comment about Medical Humour, before going on to consider the medical details about Falstaff. The type of humour which medical men share among themselves is limited in its appeal because of its medical background and content. It may be considered too salty for lay consumption. It is often elemental, and it can be bawdy, and even earthy; but it is no more so than the patients themselves, in whom largely, indeed, it has its origin. It is concerned with human nature, which, as doctors find, is not always beautiful unadorned. But it is a strongly sympathetic humour, and it is never cruel; thus it has little appeal to the prurient, and none to the prude. If it is broad, it is healthy, for the response to it is spontaneous and unrestrained. Because these special qualities of medical humour are all inherent in Falstaff, he makes a sympathetic appeal to the medical mind. He is elemental, bawdy, and earthy; and various aspects of his likeness are to be found in everyday practice. He is our familiar, and, like us, he, too, can 'turn diseases to commodity'!

The essence of his character and the secret of his timelessness lie in the fact that from the moment of his first appearance on the stage, though the audience may laugh with him or guffaw at him, never at any time does he lose either our sympathy or the attention of all who see and hear—or merely read—him. If the audience, even for a moment, should lose its sympathy for Falstaff, the nature of the character, both in his humour and his pathos, would vanish. Morgann in 1777 in his *Essay on the Dramatic Character of Sir John Falstaff* was the first to note the paradoxes in the character, which make so irresistible an appeal. Shakespeare, he writes, has

> steeped this singular character in bad habits for fifty years together, and brought him forth saturated with every folly and with every vice not destructive of his essential character, or incompatible with his own primary design! For this end, he has deprived Falstaff of every good principle; and for another . . . he has concealed every bad one. He has given him also every infirmity of body that is not likely to awaken our compassion, and which is most proper to render both his better qualities and his vices ridiculous: He has associated levity and debauch with age, corpulence and inactivity with courage, and has roguishly coupled the gout with Military honours, and a pension with the pox. He has likewise involved this character in situations, out of which neither wit or Courage can extricate him with honour.

But, for Falstaff, 'honour is a mere scutcheon'; it is much more important to him—and to his author!—that he should retain the amused interest of his audience.

We are left in no doubt about how Shakespeare meant us to see Falstaff on the stage. The description of his physique is detailed, and makes a special appeal to the medical sense of humour. The appearance usually goes with the Falstaff behaviour-pattern—the fat, jovial rascal, who is nevertheless likeable, amusing, and never long without our indulgent sympathy. It is enough that he makes us laugh.

> *Prince.* Thou art violently carried away from grace; there is a devil haunts thee in the likeness of an old fat man; a tun of a man is thy companion. Why dost thou converse with that trunk of humours, that bolting-hutch of beastliness, that swoll'n parcel of dropsies, that huge bombard of sack, that stuff'd cloak-bag of guts, that roasted Manningtree ox with the pudding in his belly, that reverend vice, that grey iniquity, that father ruffian, that vanity in years? Wherefore is he good, but to taste sack and drink it? Wherein neat and cleanly, but to carve a capon and eat it? wherein cunning but in craft? wherein crafty, but in villainy? Wherein villainous, but in all things? wherein worthy, but in nothing?
>
> *Falstaff.* I would your Grace would take me with you; whom means your Grace?
>
> *Prince.* That villainous abominable misleader of youth, Falstaff, that old white-bearded Satan.
>
> *Falstaff.* My lord, the man I know.
>
> *Prince.* I know thou dost.
>
> *Falstaff.* But to say I know more harm in him than in myself were to say more than I know. That he is old—the more the pity—his white hairs do witness it; but that he is—saving your reverence—a whoremaster, that I utterly deny. If sack and sugar be a fault, God help the wicked! If to be old and merry be a sin, then many an old host that I know is damn'd; if to be fat be to be hated, then Pharaoh's lean kine are to be loved.
>
> <div align="right">1 <i>H. IV</i>, II, 4, 430-459.</div>

Falstaff himself gives the best-remembered epitome of his character and appearance:

> *Falstaff.* Sirrah, you giant, what says the doctor to my water?
>
> *Page.* He said, sir, the water itself was a good healthy water;

but for the party that owed it, he might have more diseases than
he knew for.

Falstaff. Men of all sorts take a pride to gird at me. The
brain of this foolish-compounded clay, man, is not able to invent
anything that intends to laughter, more than I invent or is in-
vented on me. I am not only witty in myself, but the cause that
wit is in other men. I do here walk before thee like a sow that
hath overwhelm'd all her litter but one.

2 *H. IV*, I, 2, 1-14.

Again by one of the paradoxes referred to by Morgann, Falstaff
emphasises his girth to the audience, which can see and judge
for itself:

Falstaff. Bardolph, am I not fall'n away viley since this last
action? Do I not bate? Do I not dwindle? Why, my skin
hangs about me like an old lady's loose gown; I am withered
like an old applejohn.

1 *H. IV*, III, 3, 1-5.

Note again the opening words of that description of Falstaff
by himself. They are, too, the opening words of a scene. To
say the least, it is an unusual and unexpected topic, even for
an Elizabethan comedy, with which to open a scene. Is there
any significance to be attached to it? Certainly, it provides
Falstaff with the opening—which he never really needs—to
expound on himself as the source and cause of Wit. But it is
possible that it may have been also one of those topical
allusions, or, in the modern sense, a topical gag, which the
Elizabethan audience would have recognised and chuckled at.
The background for this allusion has already been discussed
(see Chap. on 'Shakespeare's Knowledge of Elizabethan
Medicine'). The statute of the College of Physicians for-
bidding the casting of urines without the presence of the
patient was probably enacted about 1601; and it is certain that
it was discussed in the College before that date. It is equally

certain that the town knew all about it. It may fairly be
deduced, therefore, that the opening line of the scene:

> Sirrah, you giant, what says the doctor to my water?

was a salacious and topical allusion, which would be recognised immediately and appreciated by the gallants surrounding
the stage and by the groundlings.

Some of Falstaff's vague ideas of physiology, particularly
of the effect of alcohol, are to be found in his justification
for drinking sack. His physiology is not so very far off the
accepted medical idea of the period, however peculiar it may
sound to us now. Falstaff is piqued that Prince John does not
believe a word of his explanation, either of his absence from
the battle or of his capture of Colville. Prince John's parting
words:

> Fare you well, Falstaff. I, in my condition,
> Shall better speak of you than you deservee. [*Exit.*]

stings Falstaff to the reply—and back into the favour of his
amused audience:

> I would you had but the wit; 'twere better than your dukedom.
> Good faith, this same young sober-blooded boy doth not love
> me; nor a man cannot make him laugh—but that's no marvel;
> he drinks no wine. There's never none of these demure boys
> come to any proof; for thin drink doth so over-cool their blood,
> and making many fish-meals, that they fall into a kind of male
> green-sickness; and then, when they marry, they get wenches.
> They are generally fools and cowards—which some of us should
> be too, but for inflammation. A good sherris-sack hath a two-
> fold operation in it. It ascends me into the brain; dries me there
> all the foolish and dull and crudy vapours which environ it;
> makes it apprehensive, quick, forgetive, full of nimble, fiery, and
> delectable shapes; which delivered o'er to the voice, the tongue,
> which is the birth, becomes excellent wit. The second property
> of your excellent sherris is the warming of the blood; which
> before, cold and settled, left the liver white and pale, which is
> the badge of pusillanimity and cowardice; but the sherris warms

it, and makes it course from the inwards to the parts extremes. It illumineth the face, which, as a beacon, gives warning to all the rest of this little kingdom, man, to arm; and then the vital commoners and inland petty spirits muster me all to their captain, the heart, who, great and puff'd up with this retinue, doth any deed of courage—and this valour comes of sherris. So that skill in the weapon is nothing without sack, for that sets it a-work; and learning, a mere hoard of gold kept by a devil till sack commences it and sets it in act and use. Hereof comes it that Prince Harry is valiant; for the cold blood he did naturally inherit of his father, he hath, like lean, sterile, and bare land, manured, husbanded, and till'd, with excellent endeavour of drinking good and good store of fertile sherris, that he is become very hot and valiant. If I had a thousand sons, the first humane principle I would teach them should be to forswear thin potations, and to addict themselves to sack.

2 H. IV, IV, 3, 83-122.

This may be Falstaff's idea of the physiology of alcohol, but it is not necessarily Shakespeare's. On two other occasions Shakespeare expresses very different views. In Othello, for example, Cassio goes to the other extreme:

> O God, that men should put an enemy in their mouths to steal away their brains! That we should with joy, pleasance, revel and applause, transform ourselves into beasts!

II, 3, 280-284.

and again in Timon of Athens:

> Rascal thieves,
> Here's gold.   Go, suck the subtle blood o' th' grape
> Till the high fever seethe your blood to froth,
> And so scape hanging.   Trust not the physician;
> His antidotes are poison, and he slays
> More than you rob.

IV, 3, 426-431.

Of the alleged effect of alcohol in producing a red nose, Falstaff is equally eloquent. Bardolph is the butt of the tirade:

Do thou amend thy face, and I'll amend my life. Thou art our admiral, thou bearest the lantern in the poop, but 'tis in the nose of thee; thou art the Knight of the Burning Lamp.

. . . .

O, thou art a perpetual triumph, an everlasting bonfire light! Thou hast saved me a thousand marks in links and torches, walking with thee in the night betwixt tavern and tavern; but the sack that thou hast drunk me would have bought me lights as good cheap at the dearest chandler's in Europe. I have maintained that salamander of yours with fire any time this two and thirty years; God reward me for it!

1 H. IV, III, 3, 24-27: 37-47.

It is only after Falstaff's death that Bardolph does give him a grudging credit for the production of the notorious nose:

    Boy. Do you not remember 'a saw a flea stick upon Bardolph's nose, and 'a said it was a black soul burning in hell?

    Bardolph. Well, the fuel is gone that maintain'd that fire: that's all the riches I got in his service.

H. V, II, 3, 40-45.

If a hero may be defined as a man who has estimated the dangers of a risk to his own person and is prepared to take that risk, then Falstaff was no hero. Falstaff certainly calculated the risks—the medical risks—and he was not prepared to take them. But that does not make him a coward. He was being prudent, as only he knew how. In the speech about Honour, he considers the medical risks of battle in some detail, and he decides that honour is not worth the risk. Honour, in his view, is a mere scutcheon—a thing of no real value, a sham, or, in its literal meaning, merely a keyhole cover; and certainly, for him, there is no honour worth a broken limb, or 'the grief of a wound'.

    Falstaff. I would 'twere bed-time, Hal, and all well.

    Prince. Why, thou owest God a death.   [*Exit.*

    Falstaff. 'Tis not due yet; I would be loath to pay him before his day. What need I be so forward with him that calls not on

me? Well, 'tis no matter; honour pricks me on. Yea, but how
if honour pricks me off when I come on? How then? Can
honour set to a leg? No. Or an arm? No. Or take away the
grief of a wound? No. Honour hath no skill in surgery, then?
No. What is honour? A word. What is in that word? Honour.
What is that honour? Air. A trim reckoning! Who hath it?
He that died o' Wednesday. Doth he feel it? No. Doth he
hear it? No. 'Tis insensible, then? Yea, to the dead. But
will it not live with the living? No. Why? Detraction will
not suffer it. Therefore I'll none of it. Honour is a mere
scutcheon. And so ends my catechism.

1 H. IV, V, 1, 125-140.

In his ordinary conversation, Falstaff often uses his knowledge of medical folk-lore, which can be regarded as part of
the prevalent gossip of the period. Shakespeare's audience
would understand and appreciate it. Much of it would not be
accepted strictly medically, but medical folk-lore rarely is in
any age. It is usually dismissed as old wives' tales. A few
instances will serve to illustrate Falstaff's medical interest, more
often than not in his own minor infirmities.

A pox of this gout! or, a gout of this pox! for the one or the
other plays the rogue with my great toe. 'Tis no matter if I do
halt; I have the wars for my colour, and my pension shall seem
the more reasonable. A good wit will make use of anything.
I will turn diseases to commodity.

2 H. IV, I, 2, 232-239.

There we have the original malingerer.

A man can no more separate age and covetousness than 'a can
part young limbs and lechery; but the gout galls the one, and
the pox pinches the other; and so both the degrees prevent my
curses.

2 H. IV, I, 2, 216-219.

And he should know, for he suffered on both counts.

It is certain that either wise bearing or ignorant carriage is caught,
as men take diseases, one of another; therefore let men take heed
of their company.

2 H. IV, V, 1, 69-71.

After he has been pulled out of the Thames, in *The Merry Wives of Windsor*, he has an additional reason for demanding sack:

> Come, let me pour in some sack to the Thames water; for my belly's as cold as if I had swallow'd snowballs for pills to cool the reins.
>
> *M. W. of W.*, III, 5, 12-16.

When Falstaff tries to play the man of acutely sensitive feelings, he becomes the more ludicrous:

> By the Lord, a buck-basket! Ramm'd me in with foul shirts and smocks, socks, foul stockings, greasy napkins, that, Master Brook, there was the rankest compound of villainous smell that ever offended nostril.
>
> *M. W. of W.*, III, 5, 80-83.

In his attempts at turning diseases to commodity, it is well to remember that Falstaff never succeeds; instead, he lands himself always deeper in trouble. Consider his attempt to deceive the Chief Justice by feigning deafness; it serves only to increase the indignation of his lordship. But Falstaff, showing no penitence for the brazen deception, regains the favour of the audience by the blatant truculence of his reply. When the servant of the Chief Justice calls to Falstaff, Falstaff tells his page to say that he is deaf. Even when the Chief Justice himself approaches Falstaff and chides him for not coming when sent for, Falstaff keeps up the pretence, and wanders on with his gossip as though he had heard nothing of what has been said, but note the sequence:

> *Falstaff.* An't please your lordship, I hear his Majesty is return'd with some discomfort from Wales.
>
> *Ch. Justice.* I talk not of his Majesty. You would not come when I sent for you.
>
> *Falstaff.* And I hear, moreover, his Highness is fallen into this same whoreson apoplexy.

Ch. Justice. Well, God mend him! I pray you let me speak with you.

Falstaff. This apoplexy, as I take it, is a kind of lethargy, an't please your lordship, a whoreson tingling.

Ch. Justice. What tell you me of it? Be it as it is.

Falstaff. It hath its original from much grief, from study, and perturbation of the brain. I have read the cause of his effects in Galen; it is a kind of deafness.

Ch. Justice. I think you are fall'n into the disease, for you hear not what I say to you.

Falstaff. Very well, my lord, very well. Rather an't please you, it is the disease of not listening, the malady of not marking, that I am troubled withal.

Ch. Justice. To punish you by the heels would amend the attention of your ears; and I care not if I do become your physician.

Falstaff. I am as poor as Job, my lord, but not so patient. Your lordship may minister the potion of imprisonment to me in respect of poverty; but how should I be your patient to follow your prescriptions, the wise may make some dram of a scruple, or indeed a scruple itself.

2 H. IV, I, 2, 97-124.

A few lines later in this scene we have one of Shakespeare's many flashes of medical imagery which so often are passed before it is realised that they are really medical gems:

I am loath to gall a new-heal'd wound.

2 H. IV, I, 2, 139.

Shakespeare's knowledge of wounds was genuine, as it is quite easy to show—almost, one might hazard, a personal experience.

In this same scene, we come to one of Falstaff's impertinences which are so diverting that we may miss the fact that they are one of Shakespeare's remarkable clinical pictures of Old Age.

Falstaff. You that are old consider not the capacities of us that are young; you do measure the heat of our livers with the bitterness of your galls; and we that are in the vaward of our youth, I must confess, are wags too.

Ch. Justice. Do you set down your name in the scroll of youth, that are written down old with all the characters of age? Have you not a moist eye, a dry hand, a yellow cheek, a white beard, a decreasing leg, an increasing belly? Is not your voice broken, your wind short, your chin double, your wit single, and every part about you blasted with antiquity? And will you yet call yourself young? Fie, fie, fie, Sir John!

Falstaff. My lord, I was born about three of the clock in the afternoon, with a white head and something a round belly. For my voice—I have lost it with hallooing and singing of anthems.

2 *H. IV*, 1, 2, 166-180.

Finally we come to the death of Falstaff. It is not seen on the stage, but the description of it is so vivid that the picture remains in our minds as clearly as if we had actually witnessed it. Shakespeare's genius for this sort of thing is so subtle that if there is any departure from his original intention in the production of the play, the whole effect is ruined. Sir Laurence Olivier in his film of Henry V made this quite unpardonable mistake. He showed the dying Falstaff, played by the aged and rather pathetic George Robey, wriggling about on his death-bed, while at the same time the words describing the death were spoken. It would not have mattered one jot if Olivier had written his own version of the play and supplied his own words; but he used Shakespeare's words. The result was that the audience were distracted in their listening by watching the antics of the old comedian, and at the same time they were also distracted from watching the distressing spectacle by trying to listen to what was being said. The effect was a complete and futile flop. It may have been Olivier's idea of good filming, but it was not Shakespeare; and it certainly was not how Shakespeare wanted the audience to remember the death of Falstaff.

Shakespeare was particularly good at deaths from the medical point of view. An interesting dissertation could be given on the deaths in the plays considered medically. It would establish beyond question how accurate Shakespeare was in his medical facts—for example, in the death of Hamlet's father (I, 5, 59-73) and also in the death of Gloucester (2 *H. VI*, III, 2, 160-167). Consider now how Shakespeare tells us about Falstaff's death. Hostess Quickly prepares us for the sad news before the actual description of the death. She comes in to tell Nym and Pistol that Falstaff is very ill.

> *Hostess.* As ever you come of women, come in quickly to Sir John. Ah, poor heart! he is so shak'd of a burning quotidian tertian that it is most lamentable to behold. Sweet men, come to him.
>
> *Nym.* The King hath run bad humours on the knight; that's the even of it.
>
> *Pistol.* Nym, thou hast spoke the right;
> His heart is fracted and corroborate.
>
> *H. V*, II, 1, 114-121.

Then after the suspense of watching an intervening scene, we have the entire description of Falstaff's death

> *Hostess.* Prithee, honey-sweet husband, let me bring thee to Staines.
>
> *Pistol.* No; for my manly heart doth earn.
> Bardolph, be blithe; Nym, rouse thy vaunting veins;
> Boy, bristle thy courage up. For Falstaff he is dead,
> And we must earn therefore.
>
> *Bardolph.* Would I were with him, wheresome'er he is, either in heaven or in hell!
>
> *Hostess.* Nay, sure, he's not in hell: he's in Arthur's bosom, if ever man went to Arthur's bosom. 'A made a finer end, and went away an it had been any christom child; 'a parted ev'n just between twelve and one, ev'n at the turning o' the tide; for after I saw him fumble with the sheets, and play with flowers, and smile upon his fingers' end, I knew there was but one way; for

his nose was as sharp as a pen, and 'a babbl'd of green fields. 'How now, Sir John!' quoth I 'What, man, be o' good cheer.' So 'a cried out 'God, God, God!' three or four times. Now I, to comfort him, bid him 'a should not think of God: I hop'd there was no need to trouble himself with any such thoughts yet. So 'a bade me lay more clothes on his feet; I put my hand into the bed and felt them, and they were as cold as any stone; then I felt to his knees, and so upward and upward, and all was as cold as any stone.

Nym. They say he cried out of sack.

Hostess. Ay, that 'a did.

Bardolph. And of women.

Hostess. Nay, that 'a did not.

Boy. Yes, that 'a did, and said they were devils incarnate.

Hostess. 'A could never abide carnation; 'twas a colour he never lik'd.

Boy. 'A said once the devil would have him about women.

Hostess. 'A did in some sort, indeed, handle women; but then he was rheumatic, and talk'd of the whore of Babylon.

Boy. Do you not remember 'a saw a flea stick upon Bardolph's nose, and 'a said it was a black soul burning in hell?

Bardolph. Well, the fuel is gone that maintain'd that fire: that's all the riches I got in his service.

H. V, II, 3, 1-45.

That description of a death is so terse in its detail and accuracy that to a medical mind there can be no doubt Shakespeare was describing a mode of death which he had actually seen more than once. This is not surprising, for though it is somewhat rare to-day, it was a type of death commonly seen in Elizabethan times. It is, indeed, the most vivid description of what we know medically as the Typhoid State. It could, for example, have been the final appearance of typhoid, or plague, or of any of the great fevers, or of peritonitis. The signs and symptoms are those of great prostration and impending death. In a medical text-book something like the following description of it will be found:

> Headache is replaced by delirium, which is occasionally violent, but more frequently of a quieter, talkative kind. The patient lies on his back, deaf, and insensible to everything around. The eyes may be closed, but sometimes they are open, and this condition, if associated with muttering, suggests that the patient is awake, while he is really almost comatose ('coma vigil'). . . . Other symptoms of intense prostration are carphology, floccillation, and subsultus tendinum.
>
> (Monro, T. K., *Manual of Medicine* (1920), p. 25).

Carphology means grasping at imaginary objects, but is sometimes used in the same sense as floccillation.

Floccillation, or floccitation (floccus, a flock of wool) means picking at the bedclothes.

Subsultus tendinum means jumping or jerking of the tendons, resulting from muscular contractions.

The appearance of the face in this state is characteristic and has been recognised as typical since Hippocrates first described it; indeed, it is known as 'facies Hippocratica':

> a sharp nose, hollow eyes, collapsed temples; the ears cold, contracted, and their lobes turned out; the skin about the forehead being rough, distended, and parched; the colour of the whole face being brown, black, livid, or lead-coloured.
>
> (Wheeler and Jack, *Handbook of Medicine* (1940), p. 311).

In a few lines Shakespeare creates a masterpiece of clinical description:

> For after I saw him fumble with the sheets, and play with flowers, and smile upon his fingers' end, I knew there was but one way; for his nose was as sharp as a pen, and 'a babbl'd of green fields.

That it had been a fever there is no doubt; Mistress Quickly tells us clearly enough:

> he is so shaken of a burning quotidian tertian, that it is lamentable to behold.

In a recent commentary, C. J. Sisson has discussed this passage. The difficulty is that in the Folio Edition 'babbl'd' is printed as 'Table'; we owe the emendation of 'babbl'd' for 'Table' to a former editor, Theobald. To-day it is fashionable to accept the Folio version of the plays as the most accurate. But the literary mind in discussing such a medical subject is apt to go off the rails slightly. For example, Sisson asks, 'Was Falstaff truly represented in this scene of his death as "babbling" in delirium?' Sisson notes that Falstaff cried out, 'God, God, God,' which, he says, is not babbling, and that ' 'a bade me lay more clothes on his feet'. He contends that this shows Falstaff was, indeed, entirely in his right mind, mindful of God and his soul's welfare, and of his bodily comfort. He admits frankly that he is offended at the notion of the unconquerable Falstaff disintegrating in mind even on his deathbed. But he ignores the fact that Falstaff also fumbled with the sheets, played with the flowers, and smiled upon his fingers' end. He ignores, in fact, the complete clinical picture to quibble on the printing of one single word. It is in such an instance that the medical approach may keep the editors right. In this particular case the medical interpretation excludes the chance of any other view.

In the correspondence columns of *The Times Literary Supplement* during May, 1958, the discussion on 'Table' or 'babbl'd' is revived by several savants. Considered medically, the death of Falstaff is a perfect clinical picture if 'babbl'd' and 'green fields' are retained; and if Shakespeare did not write them, he ought to have. Without these two words the medical image which the audience was asked to recognise does not make sense, and would not have done so to the Elizabethans, who were only too familiar with this manner of death.

Shakespeare's own death-bed scene may, indeed, have been similar to Falstaff's. Although it can only be conjecture, some facts do suggest that Shakespeare may have died from one of the typhoid fevers. Stratford-upon-Avon in those days was subjected to epidemics of such fevers after flooding from the River Avon, and the records show that the year 1616 was the most unhealthy from this cause in the early part of the century. John Ward noted, as a piece of local gossip, that

> Shakespear, Drayton, and Ben Jhonson, had a merry meeting, and itt seems drank too hard, for Shakespear died of a feavour there contracted.

That merry meeting may well have been the wedding of Shakespeare's daughter, Judith, to Thomas Quiney, on February 10th, 1616. Shakespeare's will is dated March 5th, 1616, just 49 days before his death on April 23rd, 1616. He may have felt impelled to make his will by realising the early symptoms of typhoid fever. The progressive weakness from the fever would explain the increasing feebleness of the later signatures on the will.

I wonder, too, whether Shakespeare on his death-bed recalled his own Epilogue to Henry V:

> My tongue is weary; when my legs are too,
> I will bid you good night.

Falstaff, Shakespeare wrote, shall die of a sweat, unless already ' 'a be kill'd with your hard opinions'. And die Falstaff did—

> Old, cold, wither'd, and of intolerable entrails.

5

SHAKESPEARE'S
DOCTORS, APOTHECARIES AND QUACKS

'The physician's profession, about this time, was being disentangled, on the one hand, from that of the clergyman, with which of old it had been frequently combined, and, on the other, from the trade of the apothecary—a purveyor of many things besides drugs, who was more comfortably and fashionably housed in London than was his fellow at Mantua—and from that of the barber, who united to his main functions those of dentist and yet others, announced by his long pole, painted red. The pretensions of both physicians and surgeons to a knowledge of which they fell far short were still a subject of severe censure; but little or nothing was said in or outside the profession against what was still the chief impediment to the progress of medical science—its intimate association with astrology. The physician took every care to preserve the dignity which lay at the root of much of his power, attiring himself in the furred gown and velvet cap of his doctor's degree, and riding about the streets, like his predecessor in the Middle Ages, with long foot-clothes hanging down by the side of his horse or mule. The education of physicians was carried on much like that of lawyers with care and comfort, and seems, at least sometimes, to have been deemed a suitable stage in the complete training of a gentleman.[1] The scientific and practicable value of the medical training of the day is a theme beyond the purpose of this sketch. Medical treatment, in many respects, was old-fashioned in a flattering sense of the term, in the case of new diseases it was savage; in the case of mental disease, barbarous—'a dark house and a whip'.

Sir A. W. Ward, *Cambridge History of English Literature,*
Vol. V, Ch. xiv, p. 369.

[1] Paul Hentzner (u.s.p. 31) asserts that in the fifteen colleges within and without the city of London 'members of the young nobility, gentry and others, are educated, and chiefly in the study of physic; for very few apply themselves to that of the law; they are allowed a very good table, and silver cups to drink out of'.

Chapter Five

SHAKESPEARE'S
DOCTORS, APOTHECARIES AND QUACKS

THE gradual emergence of the medical man from the priesthood is a part of medical history which need not immediately concern us here. The point at which our particular interest in this history begins is the establishment of the College of Physicians in the reign of Henry VIII. Shortly after the College had been established the break from the priesthood was complete. So much so that the College of Physicians by statute excluded any person who was in holy orders. An instance of the fact that this statute meant what it said is recorded by Dr. Goodall in the published proceedings of the College, in the prosecution of Dr. Alexander Leighton in 1617 (p. 401):

Dr. Alexander Leighton being required by the Censors to give an account by what authority he practised Physick, He told them by virtue of his Doctour's degree, which he had taken at Leyden, under Professor Heurnius. He was charged as being in Presbyter's orders, and asked why he did not stick to his Ordination. He excepted against the Ceremonies, yet owned himself as a Preacher, and acknowledged his practising Physick. In several parts whereof he was examined, but giving no satisfaction, and being perverse as to Ecclesiastical affairs, he was by the President and Censors interdicted practice. After this, endeavouring to procure a Licence, it was denied him, because in Holy Orders, the Statutes of the College declaring that none such should be admitted into the College, or permitted to practice. Whereof he was a second time forbidden practice. But he still persisting to practice in London or within seven miles, was arrested, and afterwards censured, tanquam infamis, he having been censured in the Star Chamber, and lost his ears.

This statute did not, of course, end the Church's interest

in the control of medical affairs even although the clergy were excluded from membership of the College. The Act of the 3rd *Henry VIII*, c. ii, provides that candidates for permission to practice shall first be examined, approved, and admitted by the Bishop of London, or by the Dean of St. Paul's, calling to him or them four doctors of physick; and for surgery, other expert persons in that faculty. The second clause enacts that beyond the seven-mile precinct of London, no person shall exercise or occupy, as a physician or surgeon, but if he be first approved and examined by the Bishop of the diocese, or by his Vicar-General.

The preamble of this first Act of the physicians tells enough of the state of medicine at the beginning of the sixteenth century to assure us that some such action was necessary. It reads:

> Forasmuch as the science and cunning of physick and surgery (to the perfect knowledge whereof be requisite both great learning and ripe experience) is daily within the realm exercised by a great multitude of ignorant persons, of whom the greater part have no manner of insight in the same, nor in any other kind of learning: some also can no letters on the book, so far forth that common artificers, as smiths, weavers, and women, boldly and accustomably take upon them great cures, and things of great difficulty; in the which they partly use sorcery and witchcraft, partly apply such medicines unto the disease as be very noxious, and nothing meet therefore; to the high displeasure of God, great infamy to the faculty, and the grievous hurt, damage, and destruction of many of the king's liege people; most especially of them who cannot discern the uncunning from the cunning.

An act passed in the 32nd of *Henry VIII* excepts the physician from keeping watch and ward, or the office of constable, or other office of the kind. It gives the college power to choose four of their body yearly to search the apothecaries' wares in London, and to levy a forfeiture of 100 shillings in case of an apothecary refusing to have his house searched. In *The*

Physicians of London, by Goodall, (1684), there is ample testimony to the vigour with which the college exercised their powers of fine and imprisonment upon all who invaded their rights.

Barbers and surgeons became one company by statute of the 22nd of Henry VIII. Under statutes of Edward IV and Henry VII, the barbers had been incorporated, but the surgeons 'not having any manner of corporation'. Henry VIII's Act, which incorporates both in one company, provides, however, that no barber in London shall use surgery, and no surgeon shall use the craft of shaving. The powers given to the surgeons under this statute were much inferior to those already cited as given to the physicians. The four wardens had the power to fine the offenders against the articles the sum of £5 for every month.

From a statute passed in the 34th and 35th of Henry, it appears that the powers of the surgeons had been exercised in an arbitrary and oppressive manner.

Since the making of the said Act (3rd of Henry VIII), the company and fellowship of the surgeons of London mindful only of their own lucres, and nothing the profit of the diseased or patient, have sued, troubled, and vexed divers honest persons, as well men as women, whom God hath endued with knowledge of the nature, kind, and operation of certain herbs, roots, and waters, and the using and administration of them to such as being pained with customable diseases, as women's breasts being sore, a Pin and Web in the eye, uncomes of hands, scaldings, burnings, sore mouths, the stone, strangury, saucelin and morphew, and such other diseases; and yet the said persons have not taken anything for their pains or cunning, but have ministered the same to poor people only for neighbourhood and God's sake, and of pity and charity. And it is now well known that the surgeons admitted will do no cure to any person but where they shall know to be rewarded with a greater sum than the cure extendeth unto:—

Be it enacted, that it shall be lawful to persons having knowledge and experience of the nature of herbs, roots, and waters, to practise, use, and minister to any outward sore, uncome, wound, apostemations, outward swelling, or disease; any herbs, baths, pultes, and emplaisters, according to their cunning, &c; or drinks for the stone, or strangury, or agues, without suit, vexation, trouble, penalty, or the loss of their goods; the aforesaid statute, or any Act to the contrary thereof made in any wise notwithstanding.

This act might have been entitled *The Quack's Charter*—the mountebanks of Shakespeare's time.

The apothecaries, the third branch of medicine, although they were liable to penalties inflicted by the physicians, had no separate corporation until James I granted them one in the 13th year of his reign. In the fourth year of his reign, the apothecaries had been made one corporation with the grocers of London; but in the second charter, they were separated from the grocers and given their own charter. From then on no grocer was permitted to keep an apothecary's shop. Great power was given to the apothecaries over the purchase and sale of medicines, and of entering and searching shops and houses, to discover and burn unwholesome and hurtful medicines. In their orders concerning medicines they were to advise with the President and Censors of the College of Physicians, who had special powers of their own, to 'execute the search, and view, and the due punishment of the potecaries for any their evil and fawty stuffe, without the assistance of any of the said wardens'.

The great powers of the College of Physicians involved them in much litigation, not only with the irregular practitioners whom they prosecuted and imprisoned—and who occasionally obtained a verdict against them for false imprisonment!—but also with the rival corporations of surgeons and apothecaries. Goodall states, 'there happening in the reign of Elizabeth to arise a difference between the physicians and surgeons, whether the surgeons might give inward remedies in the scrofula, French pox, or any kind of ulcer or wound', Dr. Caius so learnedly defended the rights of the physicians, that it was unanimously agreed by the Queen's Commissioners that it was unlawful for the surgeons to practice in the fore-mentioned cases.

Quarrels between the physicians and surgeons and apothecaries and quacks were frequent and bitter. They gave rise to a curious old medical literature—a class of medical polemics. In the seventeenth century the greatest exponent of this type of writing was Dr. Gideon Harvey. In 1676 he wrote *The Family Physician and the House Apothecary*. This was an attack upon the avarice and the excessive profits of the apothecaries. From the introduction we obtain an insight of the medical manners of his time.

> I have oft seen bills of apothecaries risen to 20£., and sometimes 30£., in the time of a fortnight; what is more, I have known an apothecary's bill so extravagant that the sum at the bottom of his account amounted to the sum of 50£. in the space of thirty days; when the ingredients of the whole course could not be computed to stand him in 40[-. But that which sounds worse than all this is, that not long since an apothecary of our suburbs brought in bills for less than three quarters of a year's physick to nine patients, amounting to 1,500£.

All this, he explains, was for 'the little diseases, a sweating bolus, or a potion of mithridate, for a pain in your head and limbs, coughs, stuffing in the head', etc., 'the farthest point the apothecary can safely steer'. For the greater diseases the greater remedies must be employed and for these a physician is necessary.

> Touching these great medicines, it is very fortunate they have not yet arrived to the knowledge of the little apothecaries, or the prescribing surgeons, who, using them without method, though sometimes they might do good, yet, for want of capacity in the applications, would certainly at most times do great mischiefs with them; and, therefore, every physician ought to

reserve them secret by preparing them himself; and when necessary to be used, to send them to the apothecary to be exhibited, or to give them to his patients with what directions are requisite.

More than a century earlier than Gideon Harvey, we have an actual record of the medical expenses of a Tudor household. It is recorded by V. A. J. Swain [1] from the household accounts of Sir William Petre of Ingastone Hall, Essex, Secretary of State to Henry VIII, Edward VI, and Mary (c. 1505-72). The day-to-day entries for the years 1547-62 were made by John Kyme, 'servant unto the saide Sir William Petre', and were signed by his master at the end of the financial year. Petre suffered from what was probably a varicose ulcer of the leg, which was treated from time to time with ointments:

Jan. 1549.	To Forest the Kinges surgeon by way of my masters reward for looking to my masters legge	13 s. 4 d.
	To the potycary for a purgacion for my master and for his paynes.	6 s. 8 d.
	and to Andrewes the surgeon for dressing my masters legge	6 s. 8 d.
	To Vycars the surgeon in rewards for showing my master to make the plaster called ceres plaster	6 s. 8 d.
	In rewarde to Vycars the serjeant surgeon	3 s. 4 d.

Thomas Vicary had also treated Henry VIII's 'sore legge' twenty years previously, after which, in 1528, he was appointed King's surgeon, and he influenced the royal sanction to the Act of Union of the Barbers and Surgeons in 1540.

[1] Swain, V. A. J., Anns. R.C.S. Eng. (1954), Vol. XV, 3, 193-199. *Medical Expenses in Tudor England.*

For the treatment of Sir William's deafness:

> In rewarde to Mr. Parishe man for
> bringing a plaster to lay to my
> masters feete, being good as he said
> to preserve hearing.   3 s. 4 d.
>
> To the potycary for frankensens and
> certain oyles delyvered ay Wyn-
> chester and Windsor for my masters
> ears.   3 s. 4 d.

After his retirement, Sir William suffered from some urinary
trouble for which one bill is recorded:

Aprell, 1559 To Ryche the poticarye Wednesday 5th for
madenhare 2d., scolopender 2d., a box of
unguntum album 8d., Harts tongue 1d.,
Alome 1d., for a purgacion and his paines
for bringing it, 10th day 6s. 8d.; To hym
16th day for mercury 2d., for honeysockle
water 2d., To hym 17th day for barley water
with the glas 6d., 3oz. Sirop venegar 11d.,
white sugar candye 2d., six urinalls 15d., a
skyn of rede leather 6d., To hym 19th day
for a glister and for his paines 6s. 8d. A
boxe of conserven of cheries 6d., barlie
water 4d., A boxe of oyntments 2s., a lb.
of barlie 12d., a quarte glas with water
made with barlie and certer other rotes to
make almonde mylke 12d., Allocium to gargle
with 12d., a boxe of white lozenges 12d., a
spunge 6d., barlie water 6d., Plantaine
water and honeysockle water 6d., To hym
20th day, barlie water 6d., harts tongue 2d.,
To hym 21st day barlie water a boxe of
perfome 2s. Sirop of venegar 2 oz. 8d.,
more for barlie water 4d., To hym 23rd
day barlie water 4d., 3oz. sirop of
vinegar 12d., 24th day barlie water, 25th
day barlie water 4d., 27th day halfsticke
of cassia 9d., 29th day barlie water 4d.,
last day barlie water 4d.   34 s. 5 d.

Gideon Harvey's second diatribe was published in 1683 and was called *Conclave of Physicians detecting their intrigues, plots, and frauds against their patients.* He writes:

> Know then this famous conclave is the eldest quack synagogue, consisting of a physick pope or patriarch, and a competent number of medical cardinals, who, being grown ancient, covetous and through forgetfulness ignorant, are to govern the rest, and whenever they are consulted they are to impose upon the juniors their pretended long experience, which they are to embrace with the same implicit faith the Turks do their Alcoran . . . Against those who refuse being admitted into their conclaves, and will not conform, they send forth their Bulls and anathemas, declaring them mountebanks, quacks, chymists, barbers, ignorants, &c; and if such should at any time have a patient die under their hands of an incurable disease, they thunder at it; he killed the patient, poisoned him, applied wrong medicines, and the like. According to the examination of their treasury, once in eight or ten years they proclaim a jubilee, setting open their doors to physicians, barbers, apothecaries, and renegade priests, who, upon the payment of a certain sum of chequeens, are honoured with a fop character, and received into the church porch of Aesculapius, being forbidden to enter any further during the time it is occupied by the whole Conclave or Consiglio picolo, though, at other seasons, they have toleration to peep in, or take a turn or two.

The third work of Gideon Harvey is meant to be scientific but his lively, contentious spirit bursts through. It has the impressive title *Gideonis Harvei, M.D., Medici Regis et Reginae, Ars curandi morbos expectatione, item de vanitatibus dolis et mendaciis medicorum.*' In it he classifies the physicians of the College into six groups. They are:

1. the chalybeate doctors, who cure all diseases with preparations of steel or copper;

2. the medical ass-drivers, who put all their patients upon a diet of asses' milk;

3. the jesuistical doctors, cheats 'a capite ad calcem,' who depend upon bark—Gideon's favourite aversion;
4. the medical water-bailiffs, who drench their patients at the mineral springs;
5. the butcher doctors, lanii doctores, who always phlebotomise;
6. the muck doctors, stercorarii doctores—illustrious in their greater numbers—who expel diseases by purgation.

He maintained that a practical physician may waste his time in the study of anatomy, and, unfortunately, cites William Harvey as an example—*Felicissimus anatomicus, licet medicus nequaquam insignissimus.* He states that William Harvey prescribed a purge for Lord Rainton, half the dose of which operated eighty times and the whole dose would probably have sent the patient to Hades!

We have seen that the charges made by the apothecaries were sometimes exorbitant but the Elizabethan quacks were even worse. The college had much trouble with one George Butler in 1633, because he charged 30s. a piece for 25 pills, i.e. £37 10s. Three of these pills were given to a Mrs. Style because of a sore leg. They acted promptly and she died that night! The college also prosecuted Dr. Tenant in the reign of James I because he was 'so impudent and unconscionable in the rating of his medicines that he charged one pill at £6, and an apozeme at the same price.'

It is clear that the Elizabethan physicians were men of means and of good social position, even if we judge only by the number of satirical attacks made on them. They rode in carriages which were then a luxury of the rich and great. They were clothed in velvet and wore velvet caps of a conceited cut. But most important of all, they strived to maintain, at the highest intellectual level, their knowledge of the classics and of modern languages, in addition to the current views of science and contemporary literature. Even among the men of their own time, these accomplishments were recognised as outstanding. Fuller in his *English Worthies* says of Linacre, the founder of the College, 'Returning unto England, he brought languages along with him, and was the first restorer of learning in our nation. It is questionable whether he was a better Latinist or Grecian, a better grammarian or physician, a better scholar or man for his moral deportment'. Dr. Caius, founder of the Cambridge college and another of Shakespeare's contemporaries, was of the same stamp, according to Fuller. 'I may call these two doctors the two phenixes of the profession in our nation'. The Elizabethan physician was a man of the world, whose good taste and good manners, formed by travel and learning, provided a decent cloak for his scientific ignorance. It was to this type of physician that Queen Elizabeth referred in her letter to the Emperor of Russia when she wrote recommending her physician, Dr. James:

> Quod hominum genus (medicum) quoniam et plurimarum rerum cognitionem et morum probitatem non vulgarem postulat.

Shakespeare apparently shared the Queen's views for, as we shall see, his physicians in the plays were men of similar character and calibre.

The Elizabethan surgeons, on the other hand, were a different and distinct class from the physicians. They had no statutory powers corresponding to the physicians, and they were restricted by the physicians from giving any internal medicines, even to cure external injuries. By law, the physicians could practice surgery but the surgeons could not practice medicine. An interesting commentary of this state of affairs is made by Wells (*Life of Harvey*). He is referring to the rules made by Harvey for the house officers at St. Bartholomew's Hospital:

> The doctors' treatment of the poor chirurgeons in these rules is sufficiently despotic, it must be admitted; but the chirurgeons in their acquiescence showed that they merited no better handling.

The only point on which they proved restive, indeed, was the revelation of their secrets to the physician; a great outrage, when every man had his secrets, and felt fully justified in keeping them to himself. But surgery, in the year 1633, had not shewn any good title to an independent existence. The surgeon of those days was but the hand, or instrument of the physician; the dignitary mostly applied to his famulus when he required a wen removed, or a limb lopped, or a broken head plaistered; though Harvey, it seems, did not feel himself degraded by taking up the knife or practising midwifery.

Both the College of Physicians and the College of Surgeons were united in their opposition to quacks. The physicians took a very firm stand with Walsingham, the Elizabethan statesman. Walsingham, at the command of the Queen, wrote to the College in 1551 on behalf of Margaret Kennix, 'signifying how that it was Her Highness' pleasure that the poore woman shoold be permitted by you quietly to practise and minister to the curing of diseases and wounds by the means of certain simples, in the applieing whereof it seemeth God hath given her an especiall knowledge'. In her herb-practice, she 'was restrained by the College, contrary to Her Majesty's pleasure.' 'I shall, therefore, desire you forthwith to take order among yourselves for the re-admitting her into the quiet exercise of her small talent, lest, by the renewing of her complaint to Her Majesty through your hard dealing towards her, you procure further inconveniences, therby to yourself, then perhaps you woold be willing shoold fall out'. The Physicians' reply defies both the Queen and Walsingham. 'We act', they wrote, 'under the straight band of our oth and conscience, which we esteem of greater weight than that we can release ourselves thereof at our pleasure.' They point to the 'holsome lawwes', in the carrying out of which they are 'no whit culpable for not suffering either her or any other whatsoever, to intrude themselves into so great and dangerous a vocation.' They decline to accede to his request. As to his threat, they profess themselves 'to be more willing and content to abide any inconvenience whatsoever my ensue, rather than to be brought to allow of so disorderly an attempt either in her, or in any other her lyke'. Five years later, Walsingham tackled the College again and on this occasion it was on behalf of his own medical adviser, who had the unusual name of Not—'Forasmuch as both myself have heretofore used him, and divers other gentlemen have also received good by him'. The College had committed Not to prison. Again the College refuses Walsingham's request, asserting that Not 'stubbernly (upon what encouragement we know not) of purpose infringeth our privileges, and the holsome lawes of this realme, which we by solemn oth are bound to maintain'. In 1589 Walsingham tried for the last time. He requested the release from prison of Paule Buck, who practised physick and surgery. The College's reply was a repetition of its previous refusal. Walsingham gave up and assured them that 'he would never act in anything contrary to the benefit or dignity of their society; and if upon any time by the importunity of friends he did write upon such an occasion, he, notwithstanding, left them to act what they thought most prudent'. The College of Surgeons had similar difficulties. To preserve their rights and privileges, they granted licences for a limited period only and these were not renewed if the holder had acted in any objectionable manner.

Shakespeare began to introduce doctors as characters in his plays about 1600. There are seven of these medical characters and in chronological order, they are:

Dr. Caius in *The Merry Wives of Windsor*	1600-1
The physician in *King Lear*	1605-6
The two doctors in *Macbeth*	1605-6
Cerimon in *Pericles*	1608-9
Cornelius in *Cymbeline*	1609-10
Dr. Butts in *Henry VIII*	1612-13

But although he does not appear in the play—he is dead before the action starts—we must include Gerard de Narbon (*All's Well*, 1603-4). We have, therefore, to consider Shakespeare's references to eight doctors. It may, or may not, be of some significance that no doctor appears in any of the plays until about the time when John Hall, Shakespeare's son-in-law, settled in Stratford. [1]

Dr. Caius, who is the first to appear, is not presented as a doctor but rather as a buffoon. Of him, Arthur Gray comments:

> In Master Doctor Caius, of course, we must recognise the distinguished physician, John Caius, the founder of Caius College, at Cambridge, who died in 1573. In John Hall's student days stories lingered in Cambridge of the violent quarrels of the doctor with the University officials—particularly of his vehement dislike of Sir Hugh Evans' countrymen, whom he expressly excluded from the benefit of his foundation. He was physician to Edward VI, Queen Mary and Queen Elizabeth, just as his namesake in the play was the court physician at Windsor. Otherwise there is no resemblance between the two. John Caius was not a French doctor. As an ardent Catholic he studied medicine at the Italian University of Padua.

What did Shakespeare think of the doctors he presented as doctors? How did he intend his audience to see them? There is ample evidence. The references to Gerard de Narbon alone should convince us that for the good Elizabethan physician— the member of the College—Shakespeare had the highest regard. Let him say so in his own words.

Countess. What hope is there of his Majesty's amendment?

Lafeu. He hath abandon'd his physicians, madam; under whose practices he hath persecuted time with hope, and finds no other advantage in the process but only the losing of hope by time.

[1] See Chap. 'Shakespeare and the influence of his son-in-law, Mr. John Hall, Physician.'

Countess. This young gentlewoman had a father—O, that 'had', how sad a passage 'tis!—whose skill was almost as great as his honesty; had it stretch'd so far, would have made nature immortal, and death should have play for lack of work. Would, for the King's sake, he were living! I think it would be the death of the King's disease.

Lafeu. How call'd you the man you speak of, madam?

Countess. He was famous, sir, in his profession, and it was his great right to be so—Gerard de Narbon.

Lafeu. He was excellent indeed, madam; the King very lately spoke of him admiringly and mourningly; he was skilful enough to have liv'd still, if knowledge could be set up against mortality.

All's Well, I, 1, 11-28.

> *King.*   How long is't, Count,
> Since the physician at your father's died?
> *Bertram.*   Some six months since, my lord.
> *King.*   If he were living, I would try him
>   yet—
> Lend me an arm—the rest have worn me out
> With several applications. Nature and sickness
> Debate it at their leisure.

All's Well, I, 2, 69-75.

Helena.   You know my father left me some prescriptions
Of rare and prov'd effects, such as his reading
And manifest experience had collected
For general sovereignty; and that he will'd me
In heedfull'st reservation to bestow them,
As notes whose faculties inclusive were
More than they were in note. Amongst the rest
There is a remedy, approv'd, set down,
To cure the desperate languishings whereof
The King is render'd lost.

. . . .

Countess.   But think you, Helen,
If you should tender your supposed aid,
He would receive it? He and his physicians
Are of a mind: he, that they cannot help him;
They, that they cannot help. How shall they credit

A poor, unlearned virgin, when the schools,
Embowell'd of their doctrine, have left off
The danger to itself?

   Helena.   There's something in't
More than my father's skill, which was the great'st
Of his profession, that his good receipt
Shall for my legacy be sanctified
By th' luckiest stars in heaven; and, would your honour
But give me leave to try success, I'd venture
The well-lost life of mine on his Grace's cure
By such a day and hour.

                           All's Well, I, 3, 212-221 : 226-240.

   Helena.   Gerard de Narbon was my father,
In what he did profess, well found.

   King.   I knew him.

   Helena.   The rather will I spare my praises toward him;
Knowing him is enough. On's bed of death
Many receipts he gave me; chiefly one,
Which, as the dearest issue of his practice,
And of his old experience th' only darling,
He bade me store up as a triple eye,
Safer than mine own two, more dear. I have so
And, hearing your high Majesty is touch'd
With that malignant cause wherein the honour
Of my dear father's gift stands chief in power,
I come to tender it, and my appliance,
With all bound humbleness.

   King.   We thank you, maiden;
But may not be so credulous of cure,
When our most learned doctors leave us, and
The congregated college have concluded
That labouring art can never ransom nature
From her inaidable estate—I say we must not
So stain our judgment, or corrupt our hope,
To prostitute our past-cure malady
To empirics; or to dissever so
Our great self and our credit to esteem
A senseless help, when help past sense we deem.

                           All's Well, II, 1, 100-123.

Helena's secret remedy—a habit more common among the Elizabethan surgeons than the physicians—is successful, despite the 'congregated college'. This episode recalls the attempt by Walsingham, on behalf of Elizabeth, to have Margaret Kennix recognised by the College.

The next doctor to be considered is the physician in *King Lear*. He makes a brief but effective appearance. He has little to say, but what he does say shows him to be the physician-philosopher.

> *Cordelia.* Alack, 'tis he! Why, he was met
>   even now
> As mad as the vex'd sea, singing aloud,
> Crown'd with rank fumiter and furrow weeds,
> With hardocks, hemlock, nettles, cuckoo-flow'rs,
> Darnel, and all the idle weeds that grow
> In our sustaining corn. A century send forth;
> Search every acre in the high-grown field
> And bring him to our eye.
>   What can man's wisdom,
> In the restoring his bereaved sense?
> He that helps him, take all my outward worth.
>
> *Doctor.* There is means, madam.
> Our foster-nurse of nature is repose,
> The which he lacks; that to provoke in him
> Are many simples operative, whose power
> Will close the eye of anguish.
>   *Lear*, IV, 4, I-I4.
>
> *Cordelia.*   O you kind gods
> Cure this great breach in his abused nature!
> Th' untun'd and jarring senses, O, wind up
> Of this child-changed father!
>
> *Doctor.*   So please your Majesty
> That we may wake the King; he hath slept long.
>
> *Cordelia.* Be govern'd by your knowledge, and
>   proceed
> I' th' sway of your own will.
>
> .   .   .   .

> *Doctor.*   Be by, good madam, when we do awake
>   him;
> I doubt not of his temperance.
>
> *Cordelia.*   Very well.
>
> *Doctor.*   Please you, draw near.   Louder the
>   music there!
>
> .   .   .   .
>
> *Doctor.*   Be comforted, good madam.   The
>   great rage,
> You see, is kill'd in him; and yet it is danger
> To make him even o'er the time he has lost.
> Desire him to go in; trouble him no more
> Till further settling.
>
> *Lear*, IV, 7, 14-25: 78-82.

There are two physicians in *Macbeth*.   The first merely
announces that the King will come out to touch for the King's
Evil.   It is supposed that Shakespeare included this episode
as a sop to the vanity of James I.   Shakespeare's treatment of the
character of the second doctor is, I feel, significant—a physician
who is made to appear generous, beneficent and dignified. [1]

Cornelius in Cymbeline, like the second doctor in *Macbeth*,
also finds himself in an awkward medical situation; but he is
equally circumspect and correct.

> *Queen.*   Now, Master Doctor, have you brought
>   those drugs?
>
> *Cornelius.*   Pleaseth your Highness, ay.   Here they
>   are, madam.   *Presenting a box.*
> But I beseech your Grace, without offence—
> My conscience bids me ask—whereof you have
> Commanded of me these most poisonous compounds,
> Which are the movers of a languishing death,
> But, though slow, deadly?
>
> *Queen.*   I wonder, Doctor.
> Thou ask'st me such a question.   Have I not been

[1] See Chap. 'Shakespeare and the influence of his son-in-law, Mr. John
Hall, Physician.'

Thy pupil long? Hast thou not learn'd me how
To make perfumes? distill? preserve? yea, so
That our great King himself doth woo me oft
For my confections? Having thus far proceeded—
Unless thou think'st me devilish—is't not meet
That I did amplify my judgment in
Other conclusions? I will try the forces
Of these thy compounds on such creatures as
We count not worth the hanging—but none human—
To try the vigour of them, and apply
Allayments to their act, and by them gather
Their several virtues and effects.

 Cornelius.   Your highness
Shall from this practice but make hard your heart;
Besides, the seeing these effects will be
Both noisome and infectious.

 Queen.   O, content thee. *[Enter Pisanio.*
[Aside] Here comes a flattering rascal; upon him
Will I first work. He's for his master,
And enemy to my son.—How now, Pisanio!
Doctor, your service for this time is ended;
Take your own way.

 Cornelius. [Aside] I do suspect you, madam;
But you shall do no harm.

 Queen. [To Pisanio] Hark thee, a word.

 Cornelius. [Aside] I do not like her. She doth think
       she has
Strange ling'ring poisons. I do know her spirit,
And will not trust one of her malice with
A drug of such damn'd nature. Those she has
Will stupefy and dull the sense awhile,
Which first perchance she'll prove on cats and dogs,
Then afterward up higher; but there is
No danger in what show of death it makes,
More than the locking up the spirits a time,
To be more fresh, reviving. She is fool'd
With a most false effect; and I the truer
So to be false with her.

Queen.   No further service, Doctor,
Until I send for thee.

Doctor.   I humbly take my leave.

Cymbeline, I, 5, 4-43.

In Pericles, Shakespeare makes the physician a noble lord—
a lord of Ephesus. He had two precedents for this among his
contemporaries. According to Ward (*Diary*, p. 161), 'Edmund,
Earl of Derby, who died in Queen Elizabeth's days, was
famous for chirurgerie, bone-setting and hospitalitie'. In
Shakespeare's later years, the Marquis of Dorchester, at the
age of 43, began to study physick and became a Fellow of the
College of Physicians. 'He esteemed his Fellowship in the
College, an honour second only to that of his peerage, and
maintained that his colleagues were the most learned society
in the world, and he bequeathed to them his library of the
value of £4,000, being the best at that time in any private
hand in the nation'. Shakespeare's greatest tribute to the
profession comes in this play.

    Cerimon.   I hold it ever
Virtue and cunning were endowments greater
Than nobleness and riches: careless heirs
May the two latter darken and expend;
But immortality attends the former,
Making a man a god. 'Tis known I ever
Have studied physic, through which secret art,
By turning o'er authorities, I have
Together with my practice, made familiar
To me and to my aid the blest infusions
That dwell in vegetives, in metals, stones;
And I can speak of the disturbances
That nature works, and of her cures; which doth give me
A more content in course of true delight
Than to be thirsty after tottering honour,
Or tie my treasure up in silken bags
To please the fool and death.

Gentleman.   Your honour has through Ephesus pour'd
                    forth
Your charity, and hundreds call themselves
Your creatures who, by you have been restor'd;
And not your knowledge, your personal pain, but even
Your purse, still open, hath built Lord Cerimon
Such strong renown as time shall never raze.

Pericles, III, 2, 26-48.

Shakespeare never portrays a bad doctor, although he does on two occasions make his characters refer to the possibility of an unscrupulous physician.

Bushy.   Old John of Gaunt is grievous sick,
                    my lord,
Suddenly taken; and hath sent post-haste
To entreat your Majesty to visit him.

Richard.   Where lies he?

Bushy.   Ay Ely House.

Richard.   Now put it, God, in the physician's
                    mind
To help him to his grave immediately!
The lining of his coffers shall make coats
To deck our soldiers for these Irish ware.

Richard II, I, 4, 54-62.

Kent.   Kill thy physician, and the fee bestow
Upon the foul disease.

Lear, I, 1, 163-164.

His contemporary dramatists, on the other hand, it would seem, never present a good doctor, but prefer to show them as scoundrels.

Brachiano.   Oh, the doctor!

Flamineo.   A poor quack-salving knave, my lord; one that should have been lashed for's lechery, but that he confessed a judgment, had an execution laid upon him, and so put the whip to a non plus.

Doctor.   And was cozened, my lord, by an arranter knave than myself, and made pay all the colourable execution.

Flamineo. He will shoot pills into a man's guts shall make them have more ventages than a cornet or a lamprey; he will poison a kiss; and was once minded, for his master-piece, because Ireland breeds no poison, to have prepared a deadly vapour in a Spaniard's f – – t, that should have poisoned all Dublin.

Brachiano. O, Saint Anthony's fire!

Doctor. Your secretary is merry, my lord.

Flamineo. O thou cursed antipathy to nature!—Look, his eye's bloodshed, like a needle a chirurgeon stitched a wound with, —Let me embrace thee, toad, and love thee, O thou abominable loathsome gargarism, that will fetch up lungs, lights, heart, and liver, by scruples!

Brachiano. No more.—I must employ thee, honest doctor.

> *The White Devil*, II, 1, 289-323.

 Servant. A great physician, when the Pope was sick
Of a deep melancholy, presented him
With several sorts of madmen, which wild object
Being full of change and sport, forc'd him to laugh,
And so the imposthume broke: the self-same cure
The duke intends on you.

> *The Duchess of Malfi*, IV, 2, 37-42.

 Faustus. Settle thy studies, Faustus, and begin
To sound the depth of that thou wilt profess:
Having commenc'd, be a divine in show,
Yet level at the end of every art,
And live and die in Aristotle's works.
Sweet Analytics, 'tis thus thou hast ravish'd me!
'Bene disserere est finis logices'.
Is, to dispute well, logic's chiefest end?
Affords this art no greater miracle?
Then read no more: thou hast attain'd that end:
A greater subject fitteth Faustus' wit:
Bid Economy farewell, and Galen come,
Seeing, 'Ubi desinit philosophus, ibi incipit medicus';
Be a physician, Faustus; heap up gold,
And be eternis'd for some wondrous cure:
'Summum bonum medicinae sanitas',
The end of physic is our body's health.
Why, Faustus, hast thou not attain'd that end?

Is not thy common talk found aphorisms?
Are not thy bills hung up as monuments,
Whereby whole cities have escap'd the plague,
And thousand desperate maladies been eas'd?
Yet thou art still but Faustus, and a man.
Couldst thou make men to live eternally,
Or, being dead, raise them to life again,
Then this profession were to be esteem'd.
Physic, farewell!

Doctor Faustus (Quarto of 1604).

It was the custom, in Shakespeare's day, for a physician, or
even a consultation of physicians—the congregated college—
to withdraw from a case as soon as it was apparent that no
recovery could be expected. The explanation was quite
simple. Webster states it:

Brachiano.   You are a sweet physician.

Vittoria.   Sure, sir, a loathed cruelty in ladies
Is as to doctors many funerals;
It takes away their credit.

The White Devil, I, 2, 235-238.

The warning was usually given of the impending withdrawal
by the physician explaining that he 'feared for' the patient;
or they might make the excuse that their treatment had not
been carried out.   Both Shakespeare and his contemporary
dramatists refer to this, and there are examples of both reasons.

Hastings.   The King is sickly, weak, and
                        melancholy,
And his physicians fear him mightily.

Gloucester.   Now, by Saint John, that news is bad
                        indeed.
O, he hath kept an evil diet long
And overmuch consum'd his royal person!

Richard III, I, 1, 136-139.

Worcester.   I prithee tell me, doth he keep his
                        bed?

Messenger. He did, my lord, four days ere I
        set forth;
And at the time of my departure thence
He was much fear'd by his physicians.
                                1 *Henry IV*, IV, 1, 21-24.

Sempronius. Must I be his last refuge? His friends, like
        physicians,
Thrice give him over. Must I take th' cure upon me?
                                Timon of Athens, III, 3, 11-12.

Duchess. This puts me in mind of death; physicians
        thus,
With their hands full of money, use to give o'er
Their patients.
                                The Duchess of Malfi, III, 5, 6-8.

My reason, the physician to my Love,
Angry that his prescriptions are not kept,
Hath left me, and I desperate now approve,
Desire his death, which physic did except.
                                Sonnet, CXLVII.

Ferdinand. Physicians are like kings,—they brook no
        contradiction.
                                The Duchess of Malfi, V, a, 72.

The most scathing commentary, however, is in *Volpone*.

Mosca. And since, to seem the more officious
And flatt'ring of his health, there, they have had,
At extreme fees, the college of physicians
Consulting on him, how they might restore him;
Where one would have a cataplasm of spices,
Another a flay'd ape clapp'd to his breast,
A third would have it a dog, a fourth an oil,
With wild cats' skins: at last, they all resolved
That, to preserve him, was no other means,
But some young woman must be straight sought out,
Lusty, and full of juice, to sleep by him.
                                Volpone, II, 3.

Something of Gideon Harvey's classification of doctors can
be found in both Shakespeare and his fellow dramatists.

Host. Shall I lose my doctor? No; he gives me the potions and the motions.

> *The Merry Wives of Windsor*, III, 1, 94-95.

Falstaff. Sirrah, you giant, what says the doctor to my water?

Page. He said, sir, the water itself was a good healthy water; but for the party that owed it, he might have more diseases than he knew for.

> 2 *Hen. IV*, I, 2, 1-5.

Macbeth. If thou couldst, doctor, cast
The water of my land, find her disease,
And purge it to a sound and pristine health,

I would applaud thee to the very echo,
That should applaud again. . . . .
What rhubarb, senna, or what purgative drug,
Would scour these English hence?

> *Macbeth*, V, 3, 50-56.

Timon. Go, suck the subtle blood o' th' grape
Till the high fever seethe your blood to froth;
And so scape hanging. Trust not the physician;
His antidotes are poison, and he slays
More than you rob.

> *Timon of Athens*, IV, 3, 427-431.

Ajax. I'll let his humours blood.

Agamemnon. [*Aside*] He will be the physician that
should be the patient.

> *Troilus and Cressida*, II, 3, 207-208.

Pericles. Thou speak'st like a physician, Helicanus,
That ministers a potion unto me
That thou wouldst tremble to receive thyself.

> *Pericles*, I, 2, 67-69.

Flamineo. Physicians, that cure poisons, still do work
With counter poisons.

> *The White Devil*, III, 2, 70-71.

Bosola. Doth he study physiognomy?
There's no credit to be given to th' face
Than to a sick man's urine, which some call
The physician's whore because she cozens him.

> *The Duchess of Malfi*, I, 1, 255-258.

Bosola.   Physicians that apply horse-leeches to any rank
swelling use to cut off their tails, that the blood may run through
them the faster: let me have no train when I go to shed blood,
lest it make me have a greater when I ride to the gallows.

The Duchess of Malfi, V, 2, 313-319.

Mammon.   No, he's a rare physician, do him right.
An excellent Paracelsian, and has done
Strange cures with mineral physic. He deals all
With spirits, he; he will not hear a word
Of Galen, or his tedious recipes.

The Alchemist, II, 1.

Corbaccio.   Good! he should take
Some counsel of physicians: I have brought him
An opiate here, from mine own doctor.

Mosca.   He will not hear of drugs.

Corbaccio.   Why? I myself
Stood by while it was made, saw all the ingredients:
And know, it cannot but most gently work:
My life for his, 'tis but to make him sleep.

Volpone.   [*Aside*] Ay, his last sleep, if he would take it.

Mosca.   Sir, he has no faith in physic.

Corbaccio.   Say you, say you?

Mosca.   He has no faith in physic: he does think
Most of your doctors are the greater danger,
And worse diseases, to escape. I often have
Heard him protest, that your physician
Should never be his heir.

. . . .
No, sir, nor their fees
He cannot brook: he says they flay a man,
Before they kill him.

Corbaccio.   Right, I do conceive you.

Mosca.   And then they do it by experiment;
For which the law not only doth absolve them,
But gives them great reward: and he is loth
To hire his death, so.

Corbaccio.   It is true, they kill
With as much license as a judge.

Mosca.   Nay, more;
For he but kills, sir, where the law condemns,
And these can kill him too.

Volpone, I, i.

Shakespeare refers to surgeons on only four occasions, once
only disparagingly.

Sir Toby.   Sot, didst see Dick Surgeon, sot?

Clown.   O, he's drunk, Sir Toby, an hour agone;
his eyes were set at eight i' the morning.

Sir Toby.   Then he's a rogue and a passy measures
pavin:
I hate a drunken rogue.

Twelfth Night, V, 1, 189-191.

On the three other occasions the surgeon is referred to in his
proper metier:

Portia.   Have by some surgeon, Shylock, on your charge,
To stop his wounds, lest he do bleed to death.

Merchant of Venice, IV, 1, 252-253.

Duncan.   So well thy words become thee as thy
wounds;
They smack of honour both.   Go get him surgeons.

Macbeth, I, 2, 44-45.

Benvolio.   What, art thou hurt?

Mercutio.   Ay, ay, a scratch; marry, 'tis enough.
Where is my page?   Go, villain, fetch a surgeon.

Romeo.   Courage, man; the hurt cannot be much.

Mercutio.   No, 'tis not so deep as a well, nor so wide as a
church door, but 'tis enough, 'twill serve.   Ask for me to-
morrow, and you shall find me a grave man.

Romeo and Juliet, III, 1, 89-96.

His fellow dramatists are equally reticent.

Monticelso.   They are worse,
Worse than dead bodies which are begged at gallows,
And wrought upon by surgeons, to teach man
Wherein he is imperfect.
                              The White Devil, III, 1, 97-99.

Flamineo. Would I had rotted in some surgeon's house at
Venice, built upon the pox as well as on piles, ere I had served
Brachiano!
                              The White Devil, III, 2, 9-11.

Shakespeare does not refer to the need for professional secrecy
in medical affairs and there is only one mention of it amongst
his fellows.

Wellborn. Oh, I know thy face,
Thou wert a surgeon: you must tell no tales;
Those days are done. I will pay you in private.
                     A New Way to Pay Old Debts, IV, 2, 98-100.

Friar Lawrence's speech explains clearly enough the apothecaries' beliefs in the potency of Nature's medicines.

Friar Lawrence. The gray-ey'd morn smiles on the
                              frowning night,
Check'ring the eastern clouds with streaks of light;
And fleckel'd darkness like a drunkard reels
From forth day's path and Titan's fiery wheels.
Now, ere the sun advance his burning eye
The day to cheer and night's dank dew to dry,
I must up-fill this osier cage of ours
With baleful weeds and precious-juiced flowers.
The earth that's nature's mother is her tomb;
What is her burying grave, that is her womb.
And from her womb children of divers kind
We sucking on her natural bosom find;
Many for many virtues excellent,
None but for some, and yet all different.
O, mickle is the powerful grace that lies
In plants, herbs, stones, and their true qualities;
For nought so vile that on the earth doth live
But to the earth some special good doth give;
Nor aught so good but, strain'd from that fair use,

Revolts from true birth, stumbling on abuse:
Virtue itself turns vice, being misapplied,
And vice sometime's by action dignified.
Within the infant rind of this weak flower
Poison hath residence, and medicine power;
For this, being smelt, with that part cheers each part;
Being tasted, slays all senses with the heart.
Two such opposed kings encamp them still
In man as well as herbs—grace and rude will;
And where the worser is predominant,
Full soon the canker death eats up that plant.

Romeo and Juliet, II, 3, 1-30.

Romeo's description of the starved apothecary's shop does not tally with those writers of the period who referred to 'the coach-keeping' apothecaries. But it refers to an Italian apothecary, found in the Italian story, which was Shakespeare's source. [1]

As we have seen, the apothecaries were closely supervised by the College of Physicians and no wealthy apothecary would risk getting himself into trouble by selling such a poison. But a near bankrupt apothecary would be so tempted for the sum that Romeo offered. The stuffed alligator was, of course, part of the furniture-insignia of an apothecary's shop in Elizabethan times and even later, as may be seen in the third plate of Hogarth's *Marriage-a-la-Mode*.

Romeo.   I do remember an apothecary,
And hereabouts 'a dwells, which late I noted
In tatt'red weeds, with overwhelming brows,
Culling of simples. Meagre were his looks;
Sharp misery had worn him to the bones;
And in his needy shop a tortoise hung,
An alligator stuff'd, and other skins
Of ill-shap'd fishes; and about his shelves
A beggarly account of empty boxes,
Green earthen pots, bladders, and musty seeds,

[1] Alexander, Peter (1944), *Shakespeare's Life and Art*, p. 114.

Remnants of packthread, and old cakes of roses,
Were thinly scattered, to make up a show,
Noting his penury, to myself I said
'An if a man did need a poison now,
Whose sale is present death in Mantua,
Here lives a caitiff wretch would sell it him'.
O, this same thought did but forerun my need;
And this same needy man must sell it me.
As I remember, this should be the house,
Being holiday, the beggar's shop is shut.
What, do! Apothecary!   [*Enter Apothecary.*

   Apothecary.   Who calls so loud?

Romeo.   Come hither, man. I see that thou art poor.
Hold, there is forty ducats; let me have
A dram of poison, such soon-speeding gear
As will disperse itself through all the veins
  That the life-weary taker may fall dead,
And that the trunk may be discharg'd of breath
As violently as hasty powder fir'd
Doth hurry from the fatal cannon's womb.

   Apothecary.   Such mortal drugs I have; but Mantua's
                 law
Is death to any he that utters them.

   Romeo.   Art thou so bare and full of wretchedness
And fearest to die? Famine is in thy cheeks,
Need and oppression starveth in thy eyes,
Contempt and beggary hangs upon thy back,
The world is not thy friend, nor the world's law;
The world affords no law to make thee rich;
Then be not poor, but break it and take this.

   Apothecary.   My poverty but not my will consents.

   Romeo.   I pay thy poverty and not thy will.

   Apothecary.   Put this in any liquid thing you will
And drink it off; and if you had the strength
Of twenty men, it would dispatch you straight.

   Romeo.   There is thy gold—worse poison to men's
        souls,

Doing more murder in this loathsome world
Than these poor compounds that thou mayst not sell.
I sell thee poison: thou hast sold me none.
Farewell, buy food, and get thyself in flesh.
Come, cordial and not poison, go with me
To Juliet's grave; for there must I use thee.

Romeo and Juliet, V, 1, 37-86.

That Shakespeare's fellow-dramatists had no respect for the apothecaries is quite clear.

Olympia. An ointment which a cunning alchymist
Distilled from the purest balsamum
And simplest extracts of all minerals,
In which the essential form of marble stone,
Temper'd with science metaphysical,
And spells of magic from the mouths of spirits,
With which if you but 'noint your tender skin,
Nor pistol, sword, nor lance, can pierce your flesh.

Theridamas. Why madam, think you to mock me
thus palpably?

Olympia. To prove it, I will 'noint my naked throat,
Which when you stab, look on your weapon's point,
And you shall see't rebated with the blow.

Tamburlaine the Great (2nd Pt.), IV, 2.

Subtle. Sir, against one o'clock prepare yourself;
Till when you must be fasting; only take
Three drops of vinegar in at your nose,
Two at your mouth, and one at either ear;
Then bathe your finger's ends and wash your eyes,
To sharpen your five senses, and cry 'hum'
Thrice, and then 'buz' as often; and then come.

The Alchemist, I, 1.

The nearest Shakespeare came to describing a mountebank or quack was Pinch.

Antipholus of Ephesus.   Along with them
They brought one Pinch, a hungry, lean-fac'd villain,
A mere anatomy, a mountebank,
A threadbare juggler, and a fortune-teller,

A needy, hollow-ey'd, sharp-looking wretch,
A living dead man. This pernicious slave,
Forsooth, took on him as a conjurer,
And gazing in mine eyes, feeling my pulse,
And with no face, as 'twere, outfacing me,
Cries out I was possess'd. Then all together
They fell upon me, bound me, bore me thence,
And in a dark and dankish vault at home
There left me and my man, both bound together.

Comedy of Errors, V, 1, 236-248.

Ben Jonson, however, provides an excellent impression of what the Elizabethan quacks or 'cheating mountebanks' (Webster) were like. The entire scene should be read, but the salesman's patter would sound strangely familiar in the market places of our country towns to-day.

Volpone. O, health! health! the blessing of the rich! the riches of the poor! who can buy thee at too dear a rate, since there is no enjoying this world without thee? Be not then so sparing of your purses, honourable gentlemen, as to abridge the natural course of life . . . for, when a humid flux, or catarrh, by the mutability of air, falls from your head into an arm or shoulder, or any other part; take you a ducket, or your chequin of gold, and apply to the place affected: see what good effect it can work. No, no, 'tis this blessed unguento, this rare extraction, that hath only power to disperse all malignant humours, that proceed either of hot, cold, moist, or windy causes . . . to fortify the most indigest and crude stomach, ay, were it of one that, through extreme weakness, vomited blood, applying only a warm napkin to the place, after the unction and fricace;—for the vertigine in the head, putting but a drop into your nostrils, like-wise behind the ears; a most sovereign and approved remedy: the mal caduco, cramps, convulsions, paralysies, epilepsies, tremor-cordia, retired nerves, ill vapours of the spleen, stopping of the liver, the stone, the strangury, hernia ventosa, iliaca passio; stops the dysenteria immediately; easeth the torsion of the small guts; and cures melancholia hypondriaca, being taken and applied according to my printed receipt. For, this is the physician, this the medicine; this counsels, this cures; this gives the direction,

this works the effect; and, in sum, both together may be termed
an abstract of the theorick and pratick in the Aesculapian art.
'Twill cost you eight crowns.

Volpone, II, 1.

Of course, as we know even to-day, it is given away for six-
pence! The entire hocus-pocus business of the Elizabethan
quacks is summarised for us by Ben Jonson in Nano's
amusing song.

> Had old Hippocrates, or Galen,
> That to their books put med'cines all in,
> But known this secret, they had never
> (Of which they will be guilty ever)
> Been murderers of so much paper,
> Or wasted many a hurtless taper;
> No Indian drug had e'er been famed,
> Tobacco, sassafras not named;
> Ne yet, of guacum one small stick, sir,
> Nor Raymund Lully's great elixir.
> Ne had been known the Danish Gonswart,
> Or Paracelsus, with his long sword.
> You that would last long, list to my song,
> Make no more coil, but buy of this oil.
> Would you be ever fair and young?
> Stout of teeth, and strong of tongue?
> Tart of palate? quick of ear?
> Sharp of sight? of nostril clear?
> Moist of hand? and light of foot?
> Or, I will come nearer to't,
> Would you live free from all diseases?
> Do the act your mistress pleases,
> Yet fright all aches from your bones?
> Here's the medicine for the nones.

And it is, too, perhaps an epitome of Elizabethan Medicine!

Chapter Six

SHAKESPEARE AND THE INFLUENCE OF HIS SON-IN-LAW, Mr. JOHN HALL, PHYSICIAN.

'It will be an interesting subject of enquiry, whether such of the Dramas as were written after their author entered into terms of intimate relationship with a physician, well educated in the professional knowledge of his time, bear any impression of the mental contact, since it is scarcely possible, but that some influence should have been exercised upon the impressible mind of the poet, by the husband of his favourite daughter, living with him in the same house.'

Bucknill, p. 36-37.

THE age which produced Shakespeare's plays saw also paradoxically the spread of Puritanism. 'Such a pair of facts', wrote Thomas Carlyle, 'I have rarely seen saved out of one chimerical generation'. It is rarely realised that something of this Puritanism can be studied even within the family circle of the man who wrote the plays. The source of this study is Shakespeare's own son-in-law, Mr. John Hall, Physician.

In the enormous literature on Shakespeare, very little has been written about John Hall and the possible influence he may have exerted on his father-in-law. The reason may be that it is largely a medical subject, and, therefore, it may be considered only of specialised interest. By those who do write on the subject, however, it is generally assumed that the extensive medical knowledge which Shakespeare uses throughout his plays and poems was probably acquired from John Hall. Possibly the standing and authority of such writers have led to the general acceptance of such a view. The manner in which this opinion is expressed is of interest. Sir St. Clair Thomson, talking on Shakespeare and Medicine [1] puts it this way:

[1] Thomson, Sir St. Clair, Annual Oration, London Medical Society, 1916.

When we remember that, in 1607, his eldest daughter, Susanna, married Dr. John Hall of Stratford, we readily perceive where Shakespeare had plentiful opportunities for becoming acquainted with the life, habits, and ways of thought of a medical man, and picking up a fairly intimate knowledge of the practice of medicine 300 years sgo.

In 1918, Eli Moschcowitz in an article on John Hall [1] made a similar assumption.

> Commentators have speculated freely upon where Shakespeare derived his amazing knowledge of medicine. I venture to suggest that Shakespeare was indebted largely to Dr. Hall. Certainly he knew his son-in-law for at least nine years, and perhaps longer, before he died, and probably they were no more averse to discussing professional matters with one another, than men in the same professions are to-day. Another leading circumstance is the fact . . . that most of Shakespeare's knowledge of things medical is displayed in his tragedies, most of which were written in the later years of his life.

The latter part of that statement, that most of Shakespeare's knowledge of things medical is displayed in his tragedies, is simply not true. And no less an authority on Shakespeare than Edgar I. Fripp [2] expressed a similar type of view, if only with a little more caution.

> Shakespeare from the time of his acquaintance with Dr. Hall (who was only eleven years his junior), and his proximity in Silver Street to the Barber-Surgeon's headquarters, develops a wider and more curious interest in complaints and cures, introduces . . . doctors in his dramas, and delivers himself of lay convictions derived, no doubt, from his own experience.

These statements are largely assumptions; and, so far as I know, no critical enquiry has yet been made to find out what influence, if any, Hall had in fact on Shakespeare's writings. This essay is an attempt to study the question by a critical approach to all the available facts. Hall could have influenced

[1] Moschcowitz, Eli, Bull. of Johns Hopkins Hospital, 1918. 148-152.
[2] Fripp, Edgar I., *Shakespeare, Man and Artist* (1938), II, 692.

Shakespeare's medical knowledge in two ways; either by imparting his knowledge of things medical, or by his behaviour as a doctor. We could expect, therefore, to find evidence of his influence either in Shakespeare's medical references, or in Shakespeare's characterisation of the doctors in the plays. It is necessary, in the first place, to find out the known facts about Hall, both as a doctor and as a man; then we can look at the medical references to be found in the plays and the poems; next, we can examine the doctors who appear in the plays as doctors; and, finally, we may come to some conclusions based on the evidence we find.

THE LIFE OF JOHN HALL

Who was John Hall, and what kind of man was he? His biography has been strangely neglected. Indeed, it is only in recent years that many of the facts about him have come to light. It is even necessary to correct the note written by E. K. Chambers in 1930 about his origin.

John Hall was born in 1575 in Bedfordshire and was the son of a medical practitioner. He had a brother with the unusual name of Dive, and it was this name that finally established the fact that Hall was a graduate of Cambridge and not, as Chambers records, of Oxford. John, at the age of fourteen, and his brother, Dive, matriculated at Queens College, Cambridge on the same day in 1589. [1] John took his B.A. in 1593-4 and proceeded to M.A. in 1597. Dive's record shows no progress after his matriculation, and in his father's will, 12th December, 1607, it is mentioned significantly that Dive had received his portion 'long ago'. There is evidence that after 1597 John Hall studied abroad—in France, almost certainly at Montpellier, where Rabelais had been the great medical professor. (A. Gray) [2] About 1600 he began his

[1] Venn, Dr. John, *Alumni Cantabrigiensis*, 1922.
[2] Gray, A. *Shakespeare's Son-in-law*, Heffer, Cambridge, 1939.

medical practice in Stratford-upon-Avon. In 1607 he married Shakespeare's daughter, Susanna. He died at the age of 60 on 25th November, 1635. His gravestone is second to the right of Shakespeare's in the chancel at Stratford.

There is no record of Hall ever having obtained a medical degree. He may have done so while studying abroad, but 'graduates in medicine of foreign universities had no authority to practise in England unless they had a licence from the bishop of the diocese. Until post-Reformation times episcopal registers rarely contain any mention of licences granted, and it is fairly evident that medical men seldom applied for them. There is no mention of such a grant to Hall at Worcester, and we may fairly assume that he had none'. [1] That he was qualified to practice, however, there can be no doubt, because, throughout his life, he met and consulted with his colleagues on equal terms at Oxford and a wide area around Stratford. Indeed, in his thirty-five years in Stratford, Hall built up for himself a large and extensive practice. He even attended patients as far afield as forty miles away. Fripp lists a number of the nobility, gentry and prominent citizens of Stratford and the surrounding country who were his patients. The list is provided by Hall himself in his medical notes which were published posthumously (*vide infra.*).

Any attempt to assess Hall's character must consider the two aspects of his life, the medical man and the Churchman, not because they are two distinct and separate aspects, but because the evidence available classifies itself separately under these two headings. It will be convenient, therefore, to record what is known of his medical life in the first place, and then we can note his religious convictions and their consequences.

Some indication of what kind of doctor John Hall set out to become is given in the Will of his father, William Hall. It may be inferred from the Will that the father believed his

<hr />

[1] Gray, A. *Shakespeare's Son-in-law*, Heffer, Cambridge, 1939.

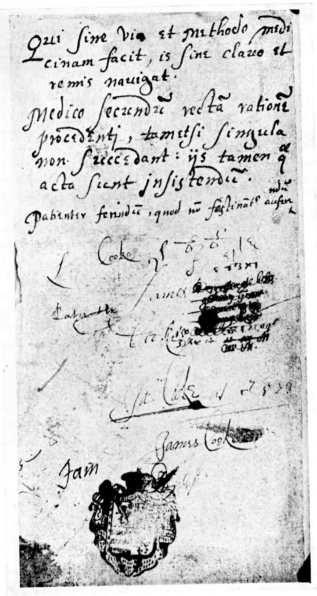

PLATE I

Photographs of Hall's own notes on Patients subsequently published as
Select Observations by Dr. James Cooke.

FIG. I

First page. Several signatures of James Cooke. I imagine the explanation is
that Dr. James Cooke had cut himself a new quill pen and that he was trying
it out as we would test a new fountain-pen to-day.

From the Eggerton Manuscripts, No. 2065.
Photographed and published by permission of the British Museum.   *facing page 94.*

PLATE I, Fig. 2
To illustrate the difficulty of deciphering Hall's Latin and his abbreviations.

From the Eggerton Manuscripts, No. 2065.
Photographed and published by permission of the British Museum.

PLATE I, Fig. 4
To illustrate the difficulty of deciphering Hall's Latin and his abbreviations.

From the Eggerton Manuscripts, No. 2065.
Photographed and published by permission of the British Museum.

son John cared only for the modern medicine of the day and had no interest in astronomy, astrology, and alchemy—the abracadabra of mediaeval medicine. John was left 'all my books on physic' but—

> 'I give and bequeath unto my man Mathew Morris all my books of astronomy and astrology. Whatsoever, conditionally that if my son John do intend and purpose to labour and study and endeavour in the said Art, that the said Matthew should instruct him in consideration of his master's benevolence and free gift.
>
> 'Further I give and bequeath all my books of Alchemy unto my foresaid servant Mathew Morris and to be paid and given presently after my decease unto him.'

But it is from his own recorded medical observations that we obtain most of our information about Hall as a doctor. In 1617, one year after Shakespeare's death, Hall, for his own information, began to record notes on the illnesses of the patients he attended together with the forms of treatment he prescribed and the results he obtained. The notes were made in Hall's own handwriting and were in an abbreviated form of Latin, which makes them very difficult to decipher. He recorded about a thousand cases, and the original manuscripts are now in the British Museum. [1] A selection of these records was subsequently published by Dr. James Cooke of Warwick in 1657, and two further editions appeared in 1679 and 1683. The title page of the book is shown facing page 96.

The story of how these private manuscripts came into Cooke's possession is told by Cooke himself in an introduction to the *Select Observations*. Cooke addresses his introduction 'To the Friendly Reader'.

Friends,

> Being in my Art an Attendent to parts of some regiments to keep the pass at the Bridge of Stratford upon Avon, There being then with me a Mate allyed to the Gentleman that writ the following Observations in Latin, he invited me to the house of Mrs. Hall,

[1] The Egerton Manuscripts, No. 2065. (British Museum).

Wife to the deceased, to see the Books left by Mr. Hall. After a view of them, she told me she had some Books left, by one that Professed Physick, with her Husband, for some mony. I told her, if I liked them, I would give her the mony again; she brought them forth, amongst which there was this with another of the Authors, both intended for the Presse. I being acquainted with Mr. Hall's hand, told her that one or two of them were her Husbands, and shewed them her; she denyed, I affirmed, till I perceived she begun to be offended. At last I returned her the mony. After some time of tryall of what had been observed, I resolved to put it to suffer according to perceived intentions, to which end I sent it to London, which after viewed by an able Doctor, he returned answer, that it might be usefull, but the Latin was so abbreviated or false, that it would require the like pains as to write a new one. After which having some spare hours, (it being returned to me) put it into this garb, being somewhat acquainted with the Authors conciseness, especially in the Receipts, having had some intimacy with his Apothecary. To compleat the number to 200. I have given the Observations of some others, wherein for your advantage, ye may observe severall under one head. It seems the Author had the happiness (if I may so stile it) to lead the way to that practice almost generally used by the most knowing, of mixing Scorbuticks in most remedies: It was then, and I know for some time after thought so strange, that it was cast as a reproach upon him by those most famous in the profession. He had been a Traveller acquainted with the French tongue, as appeared by some part of some Observations, which I got help to make English. His practice was very much, and that amongst most eminent Persons in the County where he lived, and those adjacent, as may appear by his Observations. If my pains in translating for the common good may be any wayes advantagious, it is all I look after, which shall be earnestly prayed for by

an unworthy friend
JAMES COOKE.

Post Script.

    I had almost forgot to tel ye that thes Obser. were chos n by him from all the rest of his own, which I conjectured could be no lesse than a thousand, as fittest for publique view.

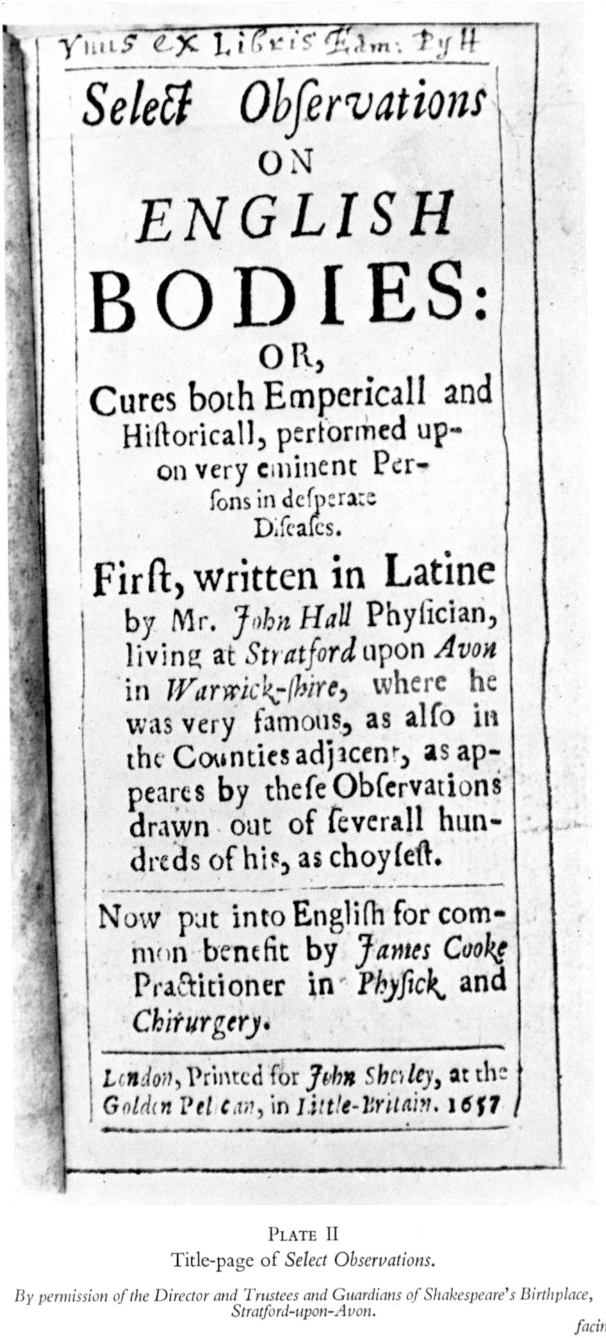

Select Observations

ON

ENGLISH

BODIES:

OR,

Cures both Empericall and Hiftoricall, performed up-- on very eminent Per- fons in defperate Difeafes.

Firft, written in Latine

by Mr. *John Hall* Phyfician, living at *Stratford* upon *Avon* in *Warwick-fhire*, where he was very famous, as alfo in the Counties adjacent, as ap- peares by thefe Obfervations drawn out of feverall hun- dreds of his, as choyfeft.

Now put into Englifh for com- mon benefit by *James Cooke* Practitioner in *Phyfick* and *Chirurgery.*

London, Printed for *John Sherley*, at the *Golden Pelican*, in *Little-Britain.* 1657

PLATE II

Title-page of *Select Observations.*

facing page 96.

PLATE III
Hall's signature from the Vestry Book.

By permission of the Director and Trustees and Guardians of Shakespeare's Birthplace, Stratford-upon-Avon.

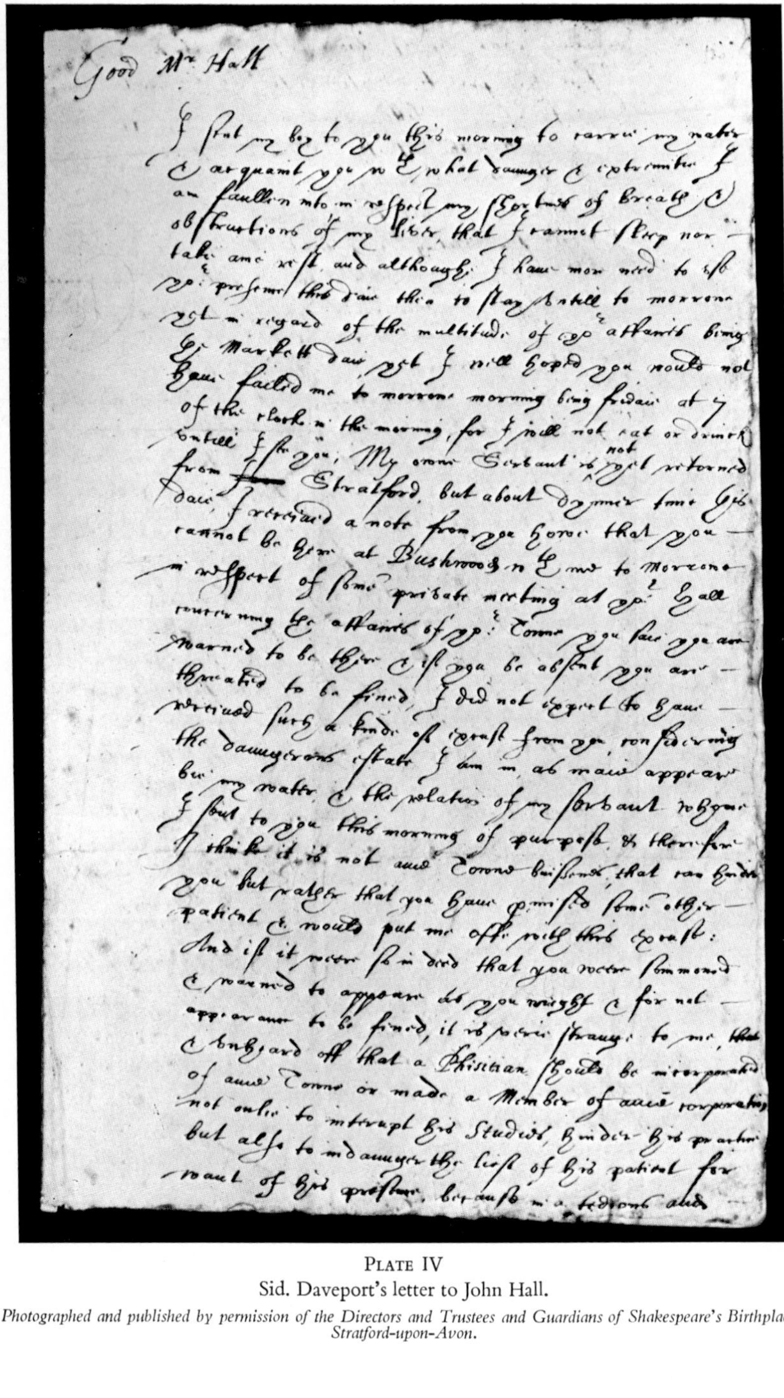

PLATE IV

Sid. Daveport's letter to John Hall.

This introduction is followed by another one addressed 'To the Judicious Reader' and written by John Bird, who describes himself as 'pridem in Academia Cantabrigiensi Medicinae Praelector Linacerianus'. Sir Humphry Rolleston[1], is doubtful about the identity of this Dr. John Bird but enters him in the list of Linacre Lecturers against 1644. Whoever he was, his introduction is worth reading—apart from the information about John Hall—if only for the medical axiom:

> 'That as Practice is the last and chiefest part of
> Physick, so is Observation the surest and most
> demonstrating part of Practice.'

Of John Hall he writes:

'A Word or two is thought fit to be said first to you Reader, for your encouragement and direction, before you begin touching both the Author and the Work. This Learned Author Lived in our time, and in the County of Warwick, where he practised Physick many years, and in great Fame for his skill, far and near. Those who seemed highly to esteem him, and whom by Gods blessing he wrought these cures upon, you shall find to be among others, Persons Noble, Rich and Learned. And this I take to be a great Signe of his ability, that such who spare not for cost, and they who have more than ordinary under-standing, nay such as hated him for his Religion, often made use of him. Many Indigent Persons, through penury, and the Brutishly foolish, through want of understanding, trust their lives to any who profess skill, and yet when oftentimes they see their errour, and finde not according to their expectation, many will to others not discover this, lest they should be derided, but praise their deceivers, which brings more into the toil. Nor is this, if we well consider, to be wondered at; and take notice, that sicknesse is commonly a punishment for Sin, which when God sends, although he deal favourably with some, it is not to be thought that Diseases are laid on onely to be taken off again. For God having determined that sicknesse shall be a Punishment, sometimes it is of one nature, other times of another; now it

[1] Rolleston, Sir Humphry, *The Cambridge Medical School: a biographical history*, p. 217. Camb. Univ. Press, 1932.

goes away itself, sometimes not without help, and when the Almighty will not have Diseases Curable, sometimes they are so in themselves, and then no Physician can cure them, as the Leprosy under the Law, and oftentimes they become so by the Patient, and often by the Physician. And so much touching the Author.'

Of the book itself, he writes:

'Particularly for this Work, it is wholy New as for the peculiar argument, Observations from English Bodies never yet extant, though very necessary. Next the Observations more General than those of most other Writers; here you meet with all sorts of diseases, there in them most commonly some of the rarest. Lastly, as I willingly give this Testimony touching their worth, so shall I be as ready to maintain my opinion if need be, They are equal to the best published; which may the rather be believed, because others commonly write such as they intended to, and have published while they have been living, and are probably unwilling to part with their best at such times; this was intended by the Author not to be published til his decease, when men more willingly part with what they have. And now Reader pardon the Translators haste, and give good heed to the escapes of the Presse, and much good may it do you.'

The Observations themselves have to-day no medical value, apart from Dr. Cooke's claim that Hall 'had the happinesse (if I may so stile it) to lead the way to that practice almost generally used by the most knowing, of mixing Scorbuticks in most remedies: it was then, and I know for sometime after thought so strange, that it was cast as a reproach upon him by those most famous in the profession'. This shows Hall as a man of an independent and original mind who had, as had all the originators of new advances in medicine, the courage to face the charge of unorthodoxy. A wide variety of cases is recorded and the treatment used is of the blunderbuss kind and quite revolting. One Observation amuses me. It is Hall's commentary on the illness of 'the excellent poet Drayton' who 'labouring of a tertian was cured by the following emetic infusions'—I spare you the details of the concoction, but the instruction ends—'add syrup of violets a spoonful, mix them'. And the Observation recorded is—'This given, wrought very well, upwards and downwards'. I had imagined that the violets were a concession to the distressed emotions of the poet but I find that Sir Thomas Browne also prescribed Syrup of Violets quite frequently. [1]

That his patients had complete faith in Dr. Hall cannot be doubted, if only from the heroic forms of treatment to which they submitted. But we have, in fact, the evidence of a letter from a patient to Dr. Hall to support this deduction. The letter explains itself. It is in Elizabethan handwriting and I give my own reading of it.

Good Mr. Hall,

 I sent my boy to you this morning to carrie my water and acquaint you with what daunger & extremitie I am faullen into in respect my shortness of breath & obstructions of my liver, that I cannot sleep nor take anie rest, and although I have more need to use yr presence this daie than to stay untill to-morrow yet in regard of the multitude of yr affairs being ye Markett daie, yet I well hoped you would not have failed me to-morrow morning being fridaie at 7 of the clock in the morning, for I will not eat or drink untill I see you. My owne Servant is not yet returned from Stratford, but about dynner time this daie I received a note from you howe that you cannot be here at Bushwood with me to-morrow in respect of some private meeting at yr Hall concerning the affairs of yr Town you saie you are warned to be there and if you be absent you are threated to be fined, I did not expect to have received such a kinde of excuse from you, considering the daungerous estate I am in, as maie appear bie my water, & the relation of my Servant whome I sent to you this morning of purpose, & therefor I think it is not anie Towne business that can hinder you but rather that you have pmsed some other patient & would put me off with this excuse: And if it were so indeed that you are sommoned & warned to appear

[1] Ketton-Cremer, R. W., *Sir Thomas Browne Prescribed*, Times Lit. Supp., Nov. 2, 1951.

as you wright & for not appearance to be fined, it is verie strange to me & unheard off that a Phisitian should be incorporated of anie Towne or made a Member of anie corporation not onlie to interupt his studies, hinder his practice but also to indaunger the liefe of his patient for want of his presence because in a tedious and daungerous disease his presence is to be preferred before his private occasions, for what cannot a daie bring fourth & a little error causeth a relapse wch is worse than the disease. I know my disease is pilous & pcrastination is daungerous. I have relied on you I trust you will not faile me now, I know you cannot be fined for visiting yr patients. Neither the Towne so barren of able men, nor the Magistrates so indiscreet to lay this burthen upon you whose profession is to be most abroad & cannot be effected by an apprentice as theirs maie, & for you to be vexed with Towne buissenes whose calling is out of Towne it would seem a great folly in you & more malice in them to requier. Therefore I councell you as a friend never be bounde as long as you may be free you shall but derogat from yr. self, heap a great deale of troubles uppon you distract you from yr. Studie wch deserveth the whole employment of anie Man, had he a 100 yeres to lyve longer: Therefore I pray you all excuses set a part that you wilbe here to-morrow morning by 7 of ye clock for I will fast until ye come and I know you cannot incurr anie daunger having so lawfull a calling. Thus with my best wishes and hartie love remembered to yr. self & ye rest of my good friendes with you. I commit you to Gods holie ptection & ever remain

Yor trewly loving frend,
& Servant
SID DAVENPORT.

My brother Colmores Phisick is ended
& all is taken he staieth at home
purposely to speak with you to-morrow
morning for further directions.
Bushwood, thursdaie, 5 July 1633.
(*Published by permission of the Director, Trustees and Guardians of Shakespeare's Birthplace, Stratford upon Avon*).

So that 300 years ago patients were very much the same self-centred, demanding, pleading, pathetic, frightened, timid spirits that we are so familiar with to-day. Notice the implicit trust he has in Hall—'for I will fast untill ye come'; but note also—'Therefore I pray you all excuses set a part that you wilbe here to-morrow morning by 7 of ye clock'. Now Bush-wood was a hamlet with a hall and a grange, 12 miles north of Stratford and Dr. Hall's only means of transport would be by horseback!

This letter of Davenport's is a convenient link between the medical and religious aspects of Hall's character. It served Hall also as a convenient but genuine excuse for failing to attend an important meeting of the Corporation on Friday, 6th July, 1633. The story is somewhat involved and goes back a few years, but it is necessary to follow it if we are to appreciate this side of Hall's life.

The Corporation of Stratford-upon-Avon was as involved as the rest of the country in the religious controversies of the day. It was the time of the spread of Puritanism. In 1619 the Vicar, Rogers, obtained an extra benefice, thus becoming a 'pluralist'. This 'lapse' was quickly seized upon by the Corporation as an opportunity for getting rid of him. They had been seeking their chance for a year or two. Permission to replace him was granted by Francis Bacon, Lord Verulam, at the time Lord Chancellor. The new incumbent chosen was Thomas Wilson from Evesham, and he came with a great reputation as a gifted preacher. His eloquence and opinions had taken puritan leaders by storm. John Hall was also greatly impressed by him. Rogers and his friends protested but the Corporation confirmed their decision to have Wilson. Partisan feelings were deeply stirred. A 'confederacy' had grown up against the Corporation and the church-wardens in favour of the easy-going and erring Vicar, Rogers. On Sunday, 30th May, 1619, Wilson, who was to be inducted the following day, attended evening service at the church. An angry mob, armed with swords, pikes, bills and stones, met him. They shouted 'Hang him, kill him, pull out his throat, cut off his pockie and burnt members, let us hale him out of the Church!' For safety Wilson was hurried into the chancel and the doors locked. But the crowd broke in and terrified the congregation. Despite all this, however, Wilson's induction took place the following day.

Wilson's popularity was considerable at the outset both with the Corporation and with Hall. The Corporation increased his salary and restored his house for him. In 1625 when he was excommunicated by Bishop Thornborough for non-conformity, the Corporation sent a deputation to Fulke Greville (Lord Brooke), the Chancellor of the Exchequer, to plead for him. In 1627 the Corporation voted £20 a year to him because of his 'learned sermons' and the 'great pains' he had taken in the pestilence which had raged in the parish. John Hall sold to the Corporation his lease tithes 'for less money than the same was worth by a hundred pounds at the least' in order to maintain the Vicar's salary at £60 and to maintain the payment of £20 per annum to the Schoolmaster (then the same salary as the Head of Eton!)

Towards the end of 1627, however, some trouble arose between the Vicar and the Corporation. The Corporation had always been very jealous about their rights to their share in the timber in the churchyard. They considered the Vicar had taken more than his share and they withdrew their grant to him of half the profits of the Churchyard. This led to serious differences. Hall supported the Vicar and in 1628-29 became his Churchwarden. In July 1629 the Corporation rescinded their grant of £20 a year to his 'wages'. Things went from bad to worse and a year or so later, there was an open breach. Sir Thomas Lucy and Sir Greville Verney were called in by the Corporation as arbitrators, 'to hear his (the Vicar's) grief and complaints' and 'wherein they have wronged or abused him'.

Hall's attitude to the Corporation had also changed. He had taken Wilson's side openly when he became his church-warden; and there are some records of the serious view he took of this office in dealing with the parishioners. Without his consent the Corporation elected him a Burgess in May, 1632, but he agreed to act. This was the third time he had been elected. On the two previous occasions he had made excuses to the Corporation and these had been accepted. He agreed now, probably in order to answer for his continued support of the Vicar and also because he was associated with the Vicar in a suit they were bringing against the Corporation. He was a member of the Corporation for sixteen months. On 30th June, 1633, he is noted in the minutes as absent and a note is added:

> Master Hall, at the last hall elected a chief-burgess of this Borough hath neglected to come to take his oath, being thereunto warned by both the Chamberlains and Serjeants.

He was summoned to attend on 6th July. It was on this occasion that, on the receipt of Sid Davenport's letter, he made the plea of urgent medical affairs and 'made default'. But on 11th July he was sworn.

It appears from the records that Hall was in dispute with the Corporation over a prolonged period and always concerning the Church and its affairs. Hall had desired to change his pew in the church from one near the pulpit—the one allotted to New Place, and thus Shakespeare's own—to another on the north side of the nave at the upper end, one which had been 'enjoyed time out of mind' by the Aldermen and their wives. The civic dignitaries were naturally annoyed with this interference in their traditional privilege. But added to this affront, Hall had spoken his mind about the Bailiff and some of the members of the Corporation. On 11 January, 1633, he was called on to submit himself and answer for his abusive speeches. Tempers arose during the year. Hall denounced the Corporation for breaking the contract with the Vicar. In spite of his sale of tithes to them on such favourable terms, they failed to increase the Vicar's stipend 'according to the intent of the Charters' and for about 10 years they had 'utterly suppressed, omitted and neglected the payment of £20 per annum to the Schoolmaster'. In addition he charged the Corporation with 'feasting and private use of the revenues'. His answer to the Corporation must have been a rousing one, and his presence at their meetings must have been spirited for, on 9th October, he was expelled from the Council for 'wilful breach of orders, sundry other misdemeanours and continual disturbances'. Shortly after this, an unseemly scuffle occurred in the Church for the possession of the pew. The bitterness between the Corporation and the Vicar increased. The key of the chancel-door of the Chapel was taken from the Vicar, thus depriving him of the passage from there to his house. He was accused of ill-using the sanctuary of the chancel by allowing his children to play ball there, to break the windows and deface the pictures, of permitting washing to be hung there, fowls to roost, and pigs to lie there. He annoyed his congregation by 'meditating his sermon' while walking in church during the service and by 'grossly particularising' in his preaching. The climax came on Tuesday, 12 May, 1635 at the funeral of Mistress Henry Smythe. The Vicar had not been asked to preach the sermon, so he sat on the pulpit steps to prevent the curate, Simon Trappe, who had been asked, from doing so. An inquiry into the whole sorry business was held on 5 June, 1635 by the Vicar-general of the diocese. The Vicar pleaded guilty to the charges and was suspended for three months. John Hall was granted his new pew:

> That the said Master Hall and his Wife and Master Nash and his Wife and Mistress Woodward and Mistress Lane should have the seat now in Question, to and for them to sit and kneel in, if the same were large enough for them.

A faculty authorising this was issued by the Bishop of Worcester, who was by now not only an old man but he was also ill. And it may, or it may not, be significant that Mr. John Hall was his medical adviser!

Perhaps, as Fripp maintains, Hall did not approve of all of Wilson's actions; probably also Hall admired the Vicar's learning and felt that he had been meanly treated; nevertheless, had Hall been a true conforming churchman he could not have overlooked Wilson's desecration of the Sanctuary. One is driven to conclude that Hall was not unduly perturbed by all the things to which Wilson pleaded guilty. And so we must infer that Hall was largely in accord with Wilson's views. We know that Hall was consulted even by those 'who hated him for his religion', which means that he not only held strong religious views but that they were well known. It is difficult, therefore, to avoid the conclusion that Hall supported the Puritan views of the Vicar.

Some further evidence of Hall as a religious man remains to be recorded from amongst the all too few available data of his life. In June, 1613, John Lane, junior, reported that Mistress Hall 'had the running of the reins' and 'had been naught with Rafe Smith at John Palmer's'. The 'defamation' was uttered in the hearing of Richard Whatcott, a signatory of Shakespeare's will, and it was duly reported. Hall prosecuted the offender at the Consistory Court of Worcester. Lane failed to appear and was excommunicated. In June, 1619, the same John Lane was in trouble again as ringleader in an attack on the vicar, Wilson, and was presented by the Churchwardens as a drunkard; thus we may have some indication of how much weight we should attach to his earlier defamatory accusations.

In August, 1633, Hall became ill with 'a burning fever which then raged killing almost all that it did infect. . . . I was not only much maciated but weakened so that I could not move

myself. . . . My wife sent for two physicians—my friends—
and I became perfectly well, praised be to God'. By the end
of September he had recovered and he records this prayer in
the Observation (LX) of his own case:

> Thou, O Lord, which hast the power of life and death, and
> drawest from the gates of death; I confess without any art or
> counsel of man, but only from Thy goodness and clemency,
> Thou hast saved me from the bitter and deadly symptoms of a
> deadly fever beyond the expectation of all about me, restoring
> me as it were from the very jaws of death to a former health:
> for which I praise thy name, O most merciful God and Father
> of our Lord Jesus Christ, praying thee to give a most thankful
> heart for this great favour for which I have cause to admire Thee.

At the time of his coronation in 1626, Charles I, not for the
first time, nor the last, was in dire need of money. He tried
the simple expedient of selling knighthoods, but you paid
whether you accepted one or not. In the Stratford area, these
Coronation knighthoods were offered to William Combe,
John Hall and Shakespeare's relation, Thomas Fulwood. All
three declined the tainted honour and were content to pay—
Hall £10, Combe £15, and Fulwood £16.

HALL AND THE SHAKESPEARE MANUSCRIPTS

It is generally agreed that by his will Shakespeare meant his
son-in-law, John Hall, to be his chief literary executor.
Susanna, Shakespeare's daughter, and her husband, Hall, were
left 'All goods, chattels, leases, plate, jewels, and household
stuff whatsoever'. It is believed that the 'leases' would include
Shakespeare's shares in the Globe and Blackfriars theatres.
There is no mention of manuscripts but Fripp maintains that
the 'household stuff whatsoever' would include his library and
manuscripts. If that is so, what happened to the manuscripts?

One comment on the subject—and I regret it is by a medical
writer—says of Hall, 'he was an avowed protestant with
puritanical leanings, which became more pronounced as he

grew older. Indeed, it is upon Hall, who was executor and, with his wife, residuary legatee of Shakespeare's will that most of the blame is laid for the loss of Shakespeare's manuscripts of his plays' [1] But another conjecture—made by J. Dover Wilson—is less excusable [2] :

'Four years were granted, who knows what ten or a dozen might have brought forth for English literature, or even whether his puritan son-in-law Dr. Hall may not have quietly suppressed 'pagan verses' found in his study of books after his death?' There are two assumptions in these statements which must be examined, first, that as residuary legatee Hall had the manuscripts of the plays and 'pagan verses' in his possession, and, secondly, that being a puritan, Hall would thus abominate all plays and would, therefore, destroy or dispose of the manuscripts of Shakespeare's plays. It is worth while considering both points in some detail. If it can be shown that the first assumption is false, the second need not be considered further.

Hall proved Shakespeare's will in London on 22 June, 1616, and with it he took an inventory of Shakespeare's goods. The actual will can still be seen in Somerset House but the inventory has disappeared. If, for the purposes of the argument, we assume for the moment that Shakespeare's manuscripts and library would be in the possession of the Halls, we might expect some reference to them in the will of John Hall or his family. But no such reference is to be found. Hall made a nuncupative will on 25 November, 1635, and the part which interests us reads:

Item concerning my study of Books, I leave them (said he) to you, my son Nash, to dispose of them as you see good. As for my manuscripts, I would have given them to Master Boles if he had been here; but forasmuch as he is not here present, you may (son Nash) burn them or else do with them what you please.

[1] Moschcowitz, Eli., *Bull. Johns Hopk. Hasp.* (1918) *xxix*, 148-152.
[2] Dover Wilson, J., *The Essential Shakespeare*, (1945), p. 139.

Fripp thinks that Master Boles was Hall's assistant and thus Hall would entrust his manuscripts and his case-books and other confidential papers to him, as one professional man to another. What actually happened to some of these manuscripts we know already from Dr. James Cooke's description of how he bought from Susanna the manuscripts of the *Select Observations*. It is clear that Susanna knew the financial value of the manuscripts. Since the First Folio edition of her father's plays had been published in 1623, she would have been well aware of the value of the manuscripts of the plays had they been in her possession.

A year and a half after John Hall's death, there is some indication of the value of his library. A member of the Corporation of Stratford, Baldwin Brookes, brought an action against John Hall's estate for the recovery of £77. He obtained a judgement for this amount. Susanna disputed the claim and prepared her answer to a bill which Brookes had filed in Chancery. In this answer she states that to satisfy his claim, Brookes had seized certain property of hers, that her late husband's goods and chattels were worth a thousand pounds, and that Brookes had sent bailiffs to the house, who 'did then and there break open the doors of the study, and rashly seize upon and take divers books, boxes, etc'. The books must therefore have been of considerable value.

In none of the subsequent wills of the family is there any mention of the manuscripts. And when we come to the last will of them all, that of Sir John Barnard who died in 1674— he was the second husband of Elizabeth, John Hall's daughter —we find that in the inventory of his goods and chattels the value set on 'all the books' in the study was £29 11s. 0d. Clearly then the manuscripts of Shakespeare's plays were not in the possession of his family.

But Shakespeare wrote his plays for his company, and it is probable that the manuscripts remained in the possession of the Lord Chamberlain's Company. Heminge and Condell were thus able to produce the First Folio. Peter Alexander clinches the argument. 'When, therefore, they declare in their address "To the great Variety of Readers",

> His mind and hand went together: And what he thought, he uttered with that easinesse, that wee have scarce received from him a blot in his papers. [1]

they are not merely mentioning a gift they admired in their friend, but indicating that the ground of their assurance that they have given the public an authoritative text is the good condition of the papers they had from Shakespeare himself.' What happened to the manuscripts that Heminge and Condell undoubtedly had access to is another mystery. There is certainly no evidence that they were ever in the possession of John Hall or his family.

Hall died on 25 November, 1635 at the age of 60. His death is recorded in the Register:

> 1635, Nov. 26. B. Johannes Hall, medicus peritissimus.

His tombstone in the chancel of the parish of Stratford bears his arms and the inscription:

> HALLIUS hic situs est medica celeberrimus arte;
>   Expectans regni Gaudia laeta Dei;
> Dignus erat meritis, qui nestora vinceret annis;
>   In terris omnes, sed rapit aequa dies.
> Ne tumulo, quid desit adest fidessima coniux,
>   Et vitae comitem nunc quoque mortis habet.

'Medicus peritissimus' and 'medica celeberrimus arte' are indeed high praise, even for tombstone eulogies. But it required the industry of American investigators to bring to light the fact that 'There is no other Stratfordian of that period whose necrological record contains eulogistic statements comparable to these'. [2]

[1] Alexander, Peter, *Shakespeare's Life and Art* (1944), pp. 27-28.
[2] The Shakespeare Documents, Vol. II, p. 588. Stanford University Press.

Hall's signature is interesting. It is quite distinctive and stands out remarkably from the other signatures in the minutes of the Vestry Book of the Parish Church. It has nothing of the flourish of the Italian handwriting of the period nor has it any of the squiggles of the native English handwriting. It is a dignified, upright, simple and solemn signature of a man who, one would hazard, had the manner of life of a puritan. It is of interest, too, to note that his daughter, Elizabeth, adopts the same style of writing.

That brief account of Hall's life records all that is known of the essential facts about him. Even so, it is possible to assess something of Hall's character from so scanty a record. It is certain that as a doctor he had an extensive practice and was trusted implicitly by rich and poor alike, even by 'such as hated him for his religion'. He had the reputation of being a highly skilled physician and he was widely known in the art and practice of medicine. It is certain, too, that he was a man of deeply religious convictions. That he hated meanness in human relationships is shown by his fight with the Stratford Corporation on behalf of the Vicar. Even if we know no more about him than that, we can write him down as a man of strong views and upright character. Beyond that bald statement it is difficult to go; the nuances of his character escape us.

E. P. Scarlett [1] attempts a more comprehensive summing-up of the man:

'The chronicle of all these trivial but very human episodes enables us to form some sort of a picture of the man who was Shakespeare's executor. The man of education and friend of the poet, the efficient business-man, the honest Puritan and church-man, the bulwark of the family, the hard-driven physician trying to reconcile medical duties and the demands made upon his time by an inconsiderate corporation, the vigorous fighter, the

[1] Scarlett, E. P., Canadian Medical Journal (1940), 43, 482-488.

physician of more than local fame—altogether a figure not unlike his sturdy contemporary of the same century, Thomas Sydenham.

. . . .

Hall was above the average level of the general practitioner of his time. He professed no surgery, leaving that to the barbers; his physiology was based upon the Hippocratic conception of the humours, comfortably buttressed by a somewhat fatalistic belief in the will of God; his clinical practice resolved itself into therapeutic ingenuity which at times is almost as overpowering to the reader as it must have been to the patient.'

Now that we know something of John Hall, we may enquire about what influence he might have had on Shakespeare. As we have already noted, he might have influenced Shakespeare in two ways—either by imparting his medical knowledge, or by the example of his own behaviour as a doctor. In the past, statements about the supposed influence of Hall have been based on mere assumptions and there has been no real study of the problem to support them. Two examples of such statements can be mentioned. Both purport to show the influence of Hall on Shakespeare in rather an unpleasant light, and both are concerned with the extravagant language of that misanthrope, Timon of Athens. The first, surprisingly, is E. I. Fripp [1], who writes,

Timon's wealth of vocabulary owes not a little, we may believe, to the poet's intercourse with Dr. Hall.

This mild and apparently harmless conjecture from such an authority becomes defamatory, however, when it is reproduced in 1949 by Ivor Brown [2] as,

Conversations with his son-in-law at Stratford would give him the lazar-house lexicon which he used so freely, and Dr. Hall, probably less scrupulous about professional confidences than such a man would be now, may have revealed to his wife's father some of his 'Select Observations' on 'English Bodies'.

An acquaintance with the life-story of John Hall is, of course,

[1] Fripp, Edgar I., *Shakespeare, Man and Artist*, II, 701.

[2] Brown, Ivor, *Shakespeare*, p. 213.

sufficient to refute this innuendo. Hall's earliest 'Observation' was not recorded until 1617, one year after Shakespeare's death. As for Hall's scruples about divulging professional confidences, there are two facts to be noted. The first has already been mentioned in Hall's Will:

> As for my manuscripts, I would have given them to Master Boles if he had been here; but forasmuch as he is not here present, you may (son Nash) burn them or else do with them what you please.

So that Hall was prepared to have his medical observations burned rather than see them fall into unsuitable hands. The second has been noted by Dr. John Bird in his introduction *To the Judicious Reader*.

> This was intended by the Author not to be published til his decease, when men more willingly part with what they have.

Both observations are surely some indication of Hall's discretion on professional matters.

In any case, is it not much more likely that Shakespeare, if he required that type of language and invective, would take the prototype from the local colour and atmosphere of the 'Winchester stews'—

> Gloucester (to the Cardinal of Winchester)
> Thou that giv'st whores indulgences to sin.
>
> 1 *H. VI*, I, 3, 35.

which surrounded his theatre life in London rather than conjecture he would obtain it from his Puritan son-in-law?

One important medical reference might possibly be due to Hall's influence. It occurs in Coriolanus, written about 1608-1609, and it concerns the story told by Menenius of the revolt of the body's members against the belly. It is, of course, Shakespeare's version of Aesop's fable. But this same story, as Bucknill notes, had been used by Rabelais. Bucknill continues,

> Malone refers to this fable as it is told by Camden, in his 'Remains'

(1605), and remarks that 'Shakespeare appears to have had Camden as well as Plutarch before him'. Rabelais, however, appears to me by far the more probable model, on account of the physiological dress in which he invests the fable, which Camden merely repeats after Aesop.

Hall, as we have noted, studied at Montpellier, where Rabelais had been famous as a professor of medicine, and would, though this is conjecture, know of the great writer's books. From Dr. James Cooke's introduction to the *Select Observations* we learn that Hall 'had been a Traveller acquainted with the French tongue, as appeared by some part of some Observations, which I got help to make English'. It is possible, therefore that Shakespeare heard this story from Hall, with 'the physiological dress', and thus Bucknill's impression may be the correct one.

Before we can begin to assess Hall's influence, however, we must know something of the extent of the medical references to be found in the Plays and Poems, and also something of the nature and value of those references. The number of references has already been mentioned and the details and the value of them can be assessed by a perusal of the various chapters in this book. The question naturally arises, where did Shakespeare obtain all this medical knowledge? A great deal of it, of course, is medical folk-lore and is part of the common inheritance, especially of country folk. But a considerable amount shows not only an astute knowledge of medical affairs but also a keen sense of the correct use of that knowledge. A proper appreciation of this aspect of the enquiry can only be made by a consideration of the various chapters of this book. Briefly, we can accept this, that Shakespeare was well acquainted with the medical knowledge of his day—and probably also with the literature. That he had some knowledge of the ancient medical writers has been shown by Bucknill, who referred to Shakespeare's use of five of the aphorisms of Hippocrates. In the chapter on the death of Hamlet's father, I have mentioned the possibility of Shakespeare's knowledge of Pliny's Natural History, from Holland's translation which was published about the time that Hamlet was written. And if we compare the medical references to be found in the plays of those of Shakespeare's contemporary dramatists already mentioned, it is interesting to note that Webster is the only one of them who can stand comparison with Shakespeare, both in quality and quantity. For example, *The White Devil* and *The Duchess of Malfi* each contain about 26 major medical references and thus, in quantity, compare with *Romeo and Juliet* which also contains 26. But though Webster may approach Shakespeare in the quantity of his medical references, his references—and those also of the other contemporaries—lack the inspired imagery, the quality of metaphor and simile, the dramatic use of the medical situation, and the accurate, terse, clinical descriptive power of Shakespeare's.

But Shakespeare was not only a busy man of the theatre, he was also very much a man of the world; and we should enquire, naturally, whether there were any sources for his medical knowledge among his London contemporaries. The first name we would think of is, of course, William Harvey. But one looks in vain for either Harvey's influence or even his views on the circulation of the blood in any of Shakespeare's plays. And the reason is not far to seek. Shakespeare died in 1616 when Harvey's views on the circulation were first made known to the College of Physicians. It was, in fact, the week before Shakespeare's death that Harvey delivered his first course of Lumleian lectures. He did not publish—*de Motu Cordis*—his book, until 1628, twelve years after Shakespeare's death. In any case, during Shakespeare's later creative period, Harvey was out of the country studying abroad.

The nearest likely source of Shakespeare's medical knowledge, one would suppose, would be his own medical son-in-law, John Hall. At this point the medical references in the plays must be examined in chronological order in relation to the incidence of Hall in Shakespeare's life.

A chart I have prepared shows the plays in chronological order. The chronology chosen is from *Shakespeare Survey* 3.

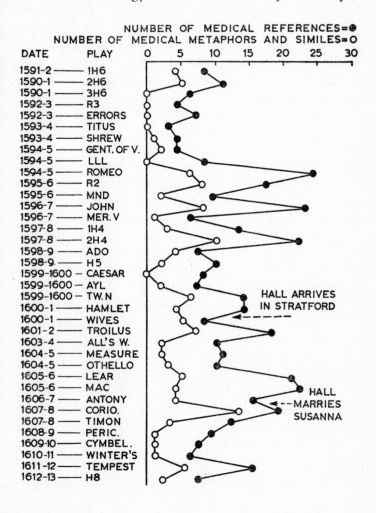

The order of the plays varies according to the authority consulted, but, in general, any other chronology still illustrates the point I want to make. Opposite each play in chronological order I have plotted the number of medical references to be found, according to my reading of them. I have marked on the chart the date on which Hall probably arrived in Stratford and also the date of his marriage to Susanna. It is obvious at once that the majority of Shakespeare's medical references occur in the plays written before Hall had ever appeared in Stratford and, therefore, before Shakespeare knew him. Up to 1600 there are 215 major medical references, between 1600 and 1607 there are 129, and after 1607 there are only 96.

It might be expected, too, that if Hall had influenced Shakespeare's medical references, some evidence would be found in Shakespeare's use of medical imagery—in his metaphors and similes. But if the numbers of the medical metaphors and similes in the plays are plotted in this same chart, the graph supports the estimate already given. Or if we consider Shakespeare's clinical descriptions, we find 49 occurring in the plays before 1600 and 30 after that date. Again, in his use of medical aphorisms, Shakespeare up to 1600 used 31 and after that date only 16. When we come to examine Shakespeare's description of the use of drugs and poisons—not merely the actual reference to the drugs themselves—there may appear to be some support for Fripp's contention, because there are 10 references before 1600 and 14 after 1600. Fripp[1] claims that 'from the time of his acquaintance with Dr. Hall', Shakespeare 'talks not only of senna and rhubarb and purgative, but of cataplasm, clyster, mandragora, poppy and fumiter, coloquintida, infusions, hemlock, mallow, hebenon'. While this is true, it is not the complete answer. It raises the question of the relative quality of those medical references. Later, Fripp's point must be

[1] Fripp, Edgar I., *Shakespeare, Man and Artist*, II, pp. 692-693.

considered in some detail. But it is clear from what has been shown statistically that, numerically, the quantity of the medical references used by Shakespeare was not influenced by his acquaintance with John Hall.

In considering the quality of the medical references we have a much more difficult problem, because it is here that one's personal opinion and preference must intervene. And it is not easy to obtain agreement on the relative quality of two comparable references because of this factor of individual preference. Over a large number of these references, however, a general agreement might be obtained, but the difficulty lies in the numbers to be considered; there are over 400 of them. We can only examine a few.

On this point of the quality of the medical references, however, let us return for a moment to Fripp's contention about Shakespeare's more frequent reference to drugs and poisons after Hall arrived in Stratford. Fripp's list of the drugs which appear in the plays written after 1600 is quite correct, but he makes no reference to the drugs mentioned in the plays written before 1600. And though there are only 10 references before 1600 compared with 14 after, it is to the quality of the pre-1600 references that I want to call attention. There is no doubt, for example, about Shakespeare's knowledge of the efficacy of ratsbane:

> I would the milk
> Thy mother gave thee when thou suck'dst her breast
> Had been a little ratsbane for thy sake.
>
> *H. 6 (1), V, 4, 27-29.*

That occurs in the first play he wrote, 1591-2.

There is, too, Shakespeare's record of how children were weaned in his day; it occurs in *Romeo and Juliet*, written in 1594-5.

> *Nurse.* And she was wean'd—I never shall
> forget it—
> Of all the days of the year, upon that day:

> For I had then laid wormwood to my dug,
> Sitting in the sun under the dove-house wall;
>
> . . . .
>
> When it did taste the wormwood on the nipple
> Of my dug, and felt it bitter, pretty fool,
> To see it tetchy, and fall out with the dug!
>
> I, 3, 25-28: 31-33.

It would seem that Shakespeare goes out of his way in *Romeo and Juliet* to let us know how much he was acquainted with the contemporary ideas on drugs and herbs and their uses. Friar Lawrence's speech (*II*, 3, 1-30) is introduced to assure the audience that the good Friar knows what he is doing when he uses drugs. So that when he tells Juliet about the drug he is giving her (*IV*, 1, 91-108), the audience feels certain that, just as Friar Lawrence has predicted,

> And in this borrow'd likeness of shrunk death
> Thou shalt continue two and forty hours,
> And then awake as from a pleasant sleep.

As if that were not enough to convince you of his knowledge of drugs and poisons, Shakespeare adds the scene between Romeo and the Apothecary to give full measure (*V*, 1, 58-86). *Romeo and Juliet* alone shows us quite clearly that Shakespeare had no need of any help from John Hall, either in the knowledge of drugs or the pharmacology of them, as it was understood in his day.

But there is still more evidence of this. In King John there is an excellent description of the action of the poison (*V*, 7, 34-48), in *Hamlet*, there are the ear drops which killed Hamlet's father—these I have discussed in another chapter; and the description of the action of the poison with which Laertes anoints the sword—the unction bought of a mountebank (*IV*, 7, 139-148). Thus it is clear that though Shakespeare did not use his knowledge of drugs and poisons as often before 1600 as he did in the tragedies written after that date, the knowledge was already there, to be used as only Shakespeare could use it. And so I cannot support Fripp's contention, either about the quantity or the quality of Shakespeare's references to drugs and poisons and his alleged indebtedness to John Hall. So far, then, it is clear that both the quantity and the quality of the medical references show no evidence of any influence of John Hall.

The next aspect to be studied is how far Hall's character as a doctor and as a man may have influenced Shakespeare. This leads us to the consideration of the doctors in the plays. The first comment to be made is that no doctor appears as a doctor in any of the plays until after 1600. There are seven characters presented in the plays as doctors; and if we are allowed to include Gerald de Narbon in *All's Well* there are eight. In chronological order they are:

1.	Dr. Caius in *The Merry Wives of Windsor*	1600-1
2.	Gerard de Narbon in *All's Well*	1603-4
3.	The physician in *King Lear*	1605-6
4.	The two doctors in *Macbeth*	1605-6
5.	Cerimon in *Pericles*	1608-9
6.	Cornelius in *Cymbeline*	1609-10
7.	Dr. Butts in *Henry VIII*	1612-13

A full discussion of the doctors in the plays will be found in the chapter on 'Doctors, Apothecaries and Quacks'. It will suffice if here I confine myself to a consideration of some aspects of the study which may have some relation to John Hall.

Gerard de Narbon had a most enviable reputation; his 'skill was almost as great as his honesty; had it stretched so far, would have made nature immortal, and death should have play for lack of work'. (*All's Well*, I, 1.) I cannot help wondering if Shakespeare's description of Gerard de Narbon influenced Hall and made him decide to record his *Select Observations*. Helena's description of her father almost suggests that deduction:

> You know my father left me some prescriptions
> Of rare and prov'd effects, such as his reading
> And manifest experience had collected
> For general sovereignty; and that he will'd me
> In heedfull'st reservation to bestow them,
> As notes whose faculties inclusive were
> More than they were in note.   *All's Well*, 1, 3, 212-218.

There is an interesting comparison to be made here between the unorthodoxy of Gerard de Narbon's prescriptions and those of John Hall, if Dr. Cooke's comment in his Introduction is accepted. Helena's prescription which is to cure the King is described by her:

> On's bed of death
> Many receipts he gave me; chiefly one,
> Which, as the dearest issue of his practice,
> And of his old experience th' only darling,
> He bade me store up as a triple eye,
> Safer than mine own two, more dear. I have so
> And hearing you high Majesty is touch'd
> With that malignant cause wherein the honour
> Of my dear father's gift stands chief in power,
> I come to tender it, and my appliance,
> With all bound humbleness.   *All Well's* II, 1, 103-113.

But since the congregated college has given its verdict against the possibility of the King being cured, the King very naturally is sceptical and hesitant:

> We thank you, maiden;
> But may not be so credulous of cure,
> When our most learned doctors leave us, and
> The congregated college have concluded
> That labouring art can never ransom nature
> From her inaidable estate—I say we must not
> So stain our judgment, or corrupt our hope,
> To prostitute our past-cure malady
> To empirics; or to dissever so
> Our great self and our credit to esteem
> A senseless help, when help past sense we deem.
>   *All's Well*, II, 1, 114-124.

Helena's argument, however, eventually persuades the King to try the remedy; perhaps that clinical truism at the end of her speech clinched it:

> Oft expectation fails, and most oft there
> Where most it promises; and oft it hits
> Where hope is coldest, and despair most fits.
>   *All's Well*, II, 1, 141-143.

In the event, of course, Helena's remedy is successful. But something similar happened in Hall's life and experience. In his Introduction to the *Select Observations*, Dr. James Cooke writes:

> 'It seems the Author had the happiness (if I may so stile it) to lead the way to that practice almost generally used by the most knowing, of mixing Scorbuticks in most remedies. It was then, and I know for some time after thought so strange, that it was cast as a reproach upon him by those most famous in the profession'.

In Macbeth two doctors are introduced. One merely announces that the King will come forth to cure the King's Evil by 'touching'. And it is supposed that Shakespeare brought in this episode as a sop to the vanity of King James. But it is to the Scottish doctor in *Macbeth* that I want particularly to draw your attention. Besides his knowledge of Medicine, I want to remark on Shakespeare's correct use of doctors in the plays and especially in what is sometimes an extremely difficult ethical situation from the doctor's angle. Here we may be seeing something of the influence of Hall's character on his father-in-law. The point I want to make is superbly illustrated in the Sleep-walking Scene. It is a very short scene of only 100 lines but I would like to go through it, considering it from the doctor's point of view, and noticing the doctor's words and reactions throughout. He has been told about the sleep-walking, but he is very sceptical and wants to see it for himself. When the scene opens he is expressing

9

his doubts about the whole business. He turns to the Queen's Lady-in-Waiting:

Doctor. I have two nights watched with you, but can perceive no truth in your report. When was it she last walk'd?

The lady tells him what she has seen.

Lady. Since his Majesty went into the field, I have seen her rise from her bed, throw her nightgown upon her, unlock her closet, take forth paper, fold it, write upon't, read it, afterwards seal it, and again return to bed; yet all this while in a most fast sleep.

The doctor comments:

Doctor. A great perturbation in nature, to receive at once the benefit of sleep and do the effects of watching! In this slumb'ry agitation, besides her walking and other actual performances, what, at any time, have you heard her say?

But the lady is too discreet to tell.

Lady. That, sir, which I will not report after her.

Whereupon you can almost hear the doctor mutter something about professional secrecy and all that, but with no success: the lady refuses to be drawn.

Doctor. You may to me; and 'tis most meet you should.

Lady. Neither to you nor any one, having no witness to confirm my speech.

At this point Lady Macbeth enters, sleep-walking, and holding a lighted taper. The doctor's first comment is one of anxiety for his patient's safety.

Doctor. How came she by that light?

The lady explains the light.

Lady. Why, it stood by her. She has light by her continually; 'tis her command.

Note there the clinical deterioration in the character of Lady Macbeth from the time when she could say in Act, I, Scene 4:

> Come, thick night,
> And pall thee in the dunnest smoke of hell,
> That my keen knife see not the wound it makes,
> Nor heaven peep through the blanket of the dark
> To cry 'Hold, hold'.

Doctor. You see her eyes are open.

Lady. Ay, but their sense is shut.

The doctor notes that Lady Macbeth rubs her hands, and the Lady slips in the suggestion that it may be "hand-washing."

> *Lady.* It is an accustomed action with her, to seem thus washing her hands; I have known her continue in this a quarter of an hour.

Lady Macbeth speaks, and the doctor, remembering as it were that his evidence must be given from records made at the time and on the spot, says:

> *Doctor.* Hark, she speaks. I will set down what comes from her, to satisfy my remembrance the more strongly.

A wise precaution, which any of you who frequent the higher courts will appreciate.

Now Lady Macbeth unconsciously reveals the crime, and the doctor suddenly realises that the horrible secret has been disclosed to the Lady-in-Waiting.

> *Lady Macbeth.* Out, damned spot! out, I say! One, two; why then 'tis time to do't. Hell is murky. Fie, my lord, fie! a soldier, and afeard? What need we fear who knows it, when none can call our pow'r to account? Yet who would have thought the old man to have had so much blood in him.

> *Doctor.* Do you mark that?

> *Lady Macbeth.* The Thane of Fife had a wife; where is she now? What, will these hands ne'er be clean? No more o' that, my lord, no more o' that; you mar all with this starting.

> *Doctor.* Go to, go to; you have known what you should not.

> *Lady.* She has spoke what she should not, I am sure of that. Heaven knows what she has known.

Lady Macbeth. Here's the smell of blood still. All the perfumes of Arabia will not sweeten this little hand. Oh, oh, oh!

The doctor's diagnostic mind is at once alert.

Doctor. What a sigh is there! The heart is sorely charg'd.

Lady. I would not have such a heart in my bosom for the dignity of the whole body.

The doctor finds himself in a dilemma—perhaps he has spoken too freely and unguardedly.

Doctor. Well, well, well.

Lady. Pray God it be, sir.

The doctor succeeds in pulling himself together, and in the hope of disguising his worst suspicions from the Lady-in-Waiting, he continues,

Doctor. This disease is beyond my practice. Yet I have known those which have walk'd in their sleep who have died holily in their beds.

But the doctor continues to be amazed at Lady Macbeth's revelation of guilt.

Lady Macbeth. Wash your hands, put on your nightgown, look not so pale. I tell you yet again, Banquo's buried; he cannot come out on's grave.

Doctor. Even so?

Lady Macbeth. To bed, to bed; there's knocking at the gate. Come, come, come, come, give me your hand. What's done cannot be undone. To bed, to bed, to bed.

Doctor. Will she go now to bed?

Lady. Directly.

By the time Lady Macbeth walks off, the doctor is so disturbed that he is thinking of many things at once, but mainly, be it noted, of his patient's welfare.

> *Doctor.* Foul whisp'rings are abroad. Unnatural
>   deeds
> Do breed unnatural troubles; infected minds
> To their deaf pillows will discharge their secrets.
> More needs she the divine than the physician.
> God, God forgive us all. Look after her;
> Remove from her the means of all annoyance,
> And still keep eyes upon her. So, good night.
> My mind she has mated, and amaz'd my sight.
> I think, but dare not speak.

But in the third scene of this Act, after he has been rebuked by Macbeth for not curing the Queen—you will recall the speech, 'Throw physic to the dogs'—the doctor does speak his mind, if only in an aside:

> *Doctor.* Were I from Dunsinane away and clear,
> Profit again should hardly draw me here.

—the truly cautious spirit that one would naturally expect to find in a physician at the Scottish Court, or, indeed, in any Scottish Physician at any Court!

It can be said of this doctor that he is a man of religious conviction—

> More needs he the divine than the physician.
> God, God forgive us all;

that the medical interest of his patient comes first with him—

> How came she by that light?

and again,

> Look after her;
> Remove from her the means of all annoyance,
> And still keep eyes upon her;

And that his behaviour in the interest of his patient was, from the point of view of medical ethics, correct; for example,

> Go to, go to; you have known what you should not

and,

Yet I have known those which have walk'd in their sleep
who have died holily in their beds.

From what we know of John Hall's character, he would
certainly fit into this picture of the good doctor with which
Shakespeare has presented us.

We may conclude, therefore, that while there is no evidence
that Hall influenced the medical references to be found in the
plays of Shakespeare, either in their quantity or their quality,
there is some evidence to suggest that, in the portrayal of
doctors as doctors in the plays, Shakespeare might have been
influenced by the character and qualities of his own doctor
son-in-law. Certainly no doctor qua doctor appears in the
plays until after Hall had arrived in Stratford; and all the
doctors in the plays are exemplary characters, entirely worthy
members of their noble profession. Like John Hall, each of
them might have been described as 'medicus peritissimus' and
also 'medica celeberrimus arte'. In the words 'precept' and
'example', I think we may sum up the influence on Shakespeare
of 'Mr. John Hall, Physician, living at Stratford upon Avon in
Warwickshire, where he was very famous'. There is, indeed,
no necessity to assume that Shakespeare's medical references,
with all their strikingly apt and amazingly rich medical
imagery, were any more influenced by a doctor than there is
to make a comparable assumption about his references to
naval and military matters, to music and the law, and the
many others. They were all the product of the mind of this
genius, Shakespeare. And who shall set bounds or limits to
the genius of Shakespeare's mind?

Sir Arthur Quiller-Couch [1] put it this way:

'Shakespeare', he wrote, 'was a miracle which I cheerfully
leave others to rationalise for you, having, for my own part
and so far as I have fared in life, found more profit in a capacity for simple wonder!'

[1] Quiller-Couch, Sir Arthur, *The Art of Writing*, p. 82.

Chapter Seven

SOME MEDICAL PROBLEMS IN
SHAKESPEARE'S TRAGEDIES.

'But the diagnoses of doctors are even less reliable when the patient is not before them than when he is'.

E. K. CHAMBERS,
William Shakespeare, Vol. I, p. 89.

TIMON OF ATHENS AND THE STATE OF SHAKESPEARE'S MIND.

WHAT was the state of mind of Shakespeare when he wrote *Timon of Athens?* There is no accurate or reliable medical evidence about it: and so these random and rambling reflections on the question must be based, as are all the opinions on the subject, on the deductions made from the play, from one's knowledge of Shakespeare, and from the history of the period. Of necessity the deductions reflect the personal bias of the writer, and the conceptions he has formed of Shakespeare. Even a cursory examination of the writers on the subject is enough to show the diversity of opinions deduced and how mere conjecture has distorted their views.

E. K. Chambers, for example, despite his great authority, frankly admits his conjecture, but goes on to express his opinion.

The temper of *Hamlet* and *Troilus and Cressida* leads up, naturally enough, to the long unrolling of the Jacobean tragedies. These are not without evidence of mental strain and sometimes exhaustion. Shakespeare's spirit must have been nearly submerged in *Lear*, and although the wave passed, and he rose to his height of poetic expression in *Antony and Cleopatra*, I think that he went under in the unfinished *Timon of Athens*. The chronology of the plays becomes difficult at this point, and it is therefore frankly a conjecture that an attempt at *Timon of Athens* early in 1608 was followed by a serious illness, which may have been a nervous breakdown, and on the other hand may have been merely the plague. Later in the year Shakespeare came to his part of *Pericles* with a new outlook. In any case the transition from the tragedies to the romances is not an evolution but a revolution. There has been some mental process such as the psychology of religion would call a conversion. Obviously the philosophy of the tragedies is not a Christian philosophy, and in a sense that of the romances is. [1]

And again—

Both *King Lear* and *Timon of Athens* seem to show symptoms of mental disturbance. But mental disturbance may come in waves. It may very likely only be a whimsy of my own that during the attempt at *Timon of Athens* a wave broke, that an illness followed, and that when it passed, the breach between the tragic and the romantic period was complete. [2]

I do not suggest that *Timon* throws much light upon Shakespeare's normal methods of working. It is, perhaps, a subjective view that he dealt with it under conditions of mental and perhaps physical stress, which led to a breakdown. [3]

Dover Wilson [4] recognises the fashion in writing about the period the play was written,

and it is certain that towards the end of the century 'melancholy' became very much the vogue both in letters and in life.

but he goes on—

look at Shakespeare's dramatic work from 1601 to 1608 as a whole, and the conclusion is, I think, irresistible that, for whatever cause, Shakespeare was subject at this time to a dominant mood of gloom and dejection, which on one occasion at least brought him to the verge of madness.

To the medical mind this is as irritating as the mother who proudly tells a doctor that her dear little boy had 'just escaped

[1] Chambers, E. K. *William Shakespeare*, Vol. I, p. 85-86.
[2] *Ibid.*, p. 274.
[3] *Ibid.*, p. 483.
[4] Dover Wilson, J., *The Essential Shakespeare*, p. 113-119.

pneumonia'; and again, to the medical mind, these 'irresistible conclusions', like the desire to scratch an itchy spot in public, must be resisted.

Dover Wilson finds also a strain of sex-nausea running through almost everything Shakespeare wrote after 1600.

> Above all in *Timon of Athens*, which breathes a hatred of mankind that rivals Swift's, nearly a whole act is devoted to the unsavoury topic. Collect these passages together, face them as they should be faced, and the conclusion is inescapable that the defiled imagination of which Shakespeare writes so often, and depicts 'in metaphor so nakedly material,' must be his own.

Shakespeare not only held a mirror up to nature, he was capable of running the whole gamut of emotions to be found in nature. But Dover Wilson must have his pet theory.

> He has fashioned a mirror of art in which, more successfully than any man before or since, he has caught the whole of Life and focused it to one intense and burning point of terror and beauty. And in so doing he found salvation. For, though the ravings of *Timon of Athens* show how near he came to plunging headlong into the abyss, *Macbeth*, which is almost a morality play, and the marvellous *Antony and Cleopatra*, in which love lifts a libertine and a harlot into the sublime atmosphere of Romeo and Juliet, prove that he kept his balance and passed on.

Shakespeare was indulging the fashion of the period when he wrote TIMON and he tells us quite clearly what he meant Timon to be. When Alcibiades asks

> Is man so hateful to thee
> That art thyself a man?

Timon leaves us in no doubt

> I am Misanthropos, and hate mankind.
> For thy part, I do wish thou wert a dog,
> That I might love thee something.
>
> IV, 3, 50-54.

And as Peter Alexander insists, 'Timon's misanthropy is the thing itself and not a form of vanity'.

G. B. Harrison discusses the point at some length. He notes [1] that the great speech which curses mankind echoes something of the earlier one of Ulysses, of Jonson's Knowell Senior, of the mad Lear, of Antony roaring at Cleopatra, and of Coriolanus. It is, as he maintains, Mad Misanthropy— but Timon's, not Shakespeare's. He notes that Timon's homily on gold, had it stood alone, would be impressive; but the theme is almost commonplace. Other dramatists had denounced gold as effectively, e.g. Johnson in Volpone and Marston in *What You Will*. He notes, too, what he calls Chambers' 'flutter of romatic fantasy'—

> It is, perhaps, a subjective view that he dealt with it under conditions of mental and perhaps physical stress which led to a breakdown.

Chambers goes on to claim, 'That the crisis took place is indisputable', but the blunt assertion loses something of its authority when it is followed almost immediately by the sentence—

> It is tempting to suppose that the deep waters closed over Shakespeare's head while he was still elaborating the play, and that when he faced the world once more in his new mood the inclination to finish the task had left him.

Harrison concedes that modern critics and scholars may have reacted too far against the philosophising of Bradley and Dowden, and may be too prone to consider Shakespeare merely a man of the theatre who knew all the tricks of the trade, and was primarily concerned with attracting a crowd: and, it may be added, writing Misanthropies, if his employers thought that was what their patrons wanted!

Whatever the doubts and heartburnings of the litterateurs about the condition of Shakespeare's mind, none of them pin-point any part of Timon and assert that when he wrote that particular part of it he was unbalanced mentally. From

[1] Harrison, G. B., *Shakespeare's Tragedies*, p. 261.

the medical approach, there is no part of the play which can be said to be the writing of an unbalanced mind. I write not as a psychiatrist but as an ordinary medical; but I know of no psychiatrist who agrees with the literary pundits who doubt Shakespeare's sanity.

E. K. Chambers would not, of course, accept the medical approach. He has made his position about doctors quite clear—

> the diagnoses of doctors are even less reliable when the patient is not before them than when he is.

Are the scientific doctors of the future going to interpret this little bit of clownish facetiousness as evidence of some degree of a psychiatric euphoria?

He makes this assertion when he accepts the account of Shakespeare's death as given by Rev. John Ward. Ward had recorded that

> Shakespear, Drayton, and Ben Jhonson, had a merry meeting, and itt seems drank too hard, for Shakespear died of a feavour there contracted.

and Chambers comments, 'There is no reason to reject this report. Ward had been a student of medicine, and became vicar of Stratford in 1662'. It is enlightening to realise that, in the mind of this literary pundit, the jottings of parish gossip by the Vicar, who is also a 'failed M.D.', are accepted as evidence, because he finds no reason to reject them; I should have thought there was equally no reason to accept them. Indeed, there is some definite medical evidence of a different cause for Shakespeare's death. [1]

Some years ago when I became interested in this problem and had accepted the opinion of the literary authorities that Shakespeare may have been unbalanced, I tried to satisfy myself about the nature of the malady. The clue, I thought then, might be in Ward's report of Shakespeare's death, that he died of a fever following a drinking-bout with his friends

[1] See Chap. on *The Medical History of Sir John Falstaff*

Drayton and Jonson. If so, there may have been previous drinking bouts in his life. Had there been, there might also have been, during a period of excess, a state of alcoholism, not amounting to delirium tremens, but a variation of it known as Korsakoff's syndrome. In this condition the patient suffers mental changes and turns against his intimate friends. I thought this might explain the misanthropy and the tirades of Timon. I found his references to drinking were themselves tirades against drinking, e.g.

> Here's that which is too weak to be a sinner, honest water, which ne'er left man i' th' mire.
>
> *Timon,* I, 2, 56-57.

> We make ourselves fools to disport ourselves,
> And spend our flatteries to drink those men
> Upon whose age we void it up again
> With poisonous spite and envy.
>
> *Timon,* I, 2, 130-134.

> Go, suck the subtle blood o' th' grape
> Till the high fever seethe your blood to froth,
> And so scape hanging. Trust not the physician;
> His antidotes are poison, and he slays
> Moe than you rob.
>
> *Timon,* IV, 3, 427-431.

A cursory examination suggested, therefore, that the play might have been written during a period of depression and remorse following a bout of alcoholism. But when I submitted my ideas to some friends who were psychiatrists, I found that they were all agreed that there was no medical evidence in the play of any mental imbalance. Having re-read the play many times, and in the light of the history of the period and the fashion in contemporary play-writing, I am now persuaded they are right.

But to the non-medical reader, no doubt, certain of the speeches with medical references—medical tirades—will need some explaining away before they can accept that view. The

several speeches in which Timon calls down epidemics of
dreadful disease need not all be considered. From the medical
point of view, one speech, however, must be commented on:

> Consumptions sow
> In hollow bones of man; strike their sharp shins;
> And mar men's spurring. Crack the lawyer's voice,
> That he may never more false title plead,
> Nor sound his quillets shrilly. Hoar the flamen,
> That scolds against the quality of flesh
> And not believes himself. Down with the nose,
> Down with it flat, take the bridge quite away
> Of him that, his particular to foresee,
> Smells from the general weal. Make curl'd-pate ruffians bald,
> And let the unscarr'd braggarts of the war
> Derive some pain from you. Plague all,
> That your activity may defeat and quell
> The source of all erection. There's more gold.
> Do you damn others, and let this damn you,
> And ditches grave you all!
>
> *Timon*, IV, 3, 150-165.

This is delivered to the two courtesans. Shakespeare was
certainly familiar with this type of woman. They lived in the
brothels—the Winchester stews—which surrounded the
theatres on the South Bank. He could not have failed to see
for himself the results of contact with these Winchester geese.
Venereal disease was appallingly common in London at that
time. It is strange that to-day, as a result of the introduction
of Penicillin, even medical students may not recognise that
speech for what it is. It is, in fact, an accurate description of
the late effects of syphilis, and it was a daily sight in the streets
of London. Shakespeare was not describing the condition in
medical terms; he is describing what he himself saw, and he
is doing so in his own language. The result is as accurate as
any medical description could be, and much more vivid and
memorable.

When we recall the dreadful curses that Timon wished to

fall on Athens, we should also remember that set in the middle of them is the gem of his definition of law and orderliness— a most striking contrast, and certainly abundant evidence of a balanced mind:

> Piety and fear,
> Religion to the gods, peace, justice, truth,
> Domestic awe, night-rest, and neighbourhood,
> Instruction, manners, mysteries, and trades,
> Degrees, observances, customs and laws.

Shakespeare, when he wrote Timon of Athens for the King's Men, was commenting on the times and the conditions— especially at the Court—which surrounded him. The mood of his writing was in the current fashion. Perhaps the real theme of the play, and the clue to it, is given to us by Apemantus in the first scene of the first act:

> That there should be small love amongst these sweet knaves,
> And all this courtesy! The strain of man's bred out
> Into baboon and monkey.
>
> I, 1, 251-253.

A strange commentary! But if what is recorded of the times —and the Court—is accurate, it is a strange commentary, indeed; and it is true! And strange as it is, it is no more weird than the story of 'the wisest fool in Christendom', in whose reign the play was written and by a man who had some knowledge of what went on inside that Court.

THE DEATH OF HAMLET'S FATHER

How did *Hamlet's* father die? It is a fair medico-legal question and one to which a reasoned medical answer should be expected. In the play, we are told by the Ghost, drops were poured into his ears while he was asleep, and these drops caused his death. We accept the fact of his death without questioning and we go on to the rest of the play without pausing to satisfy ourselves that death could be caused in such a way. As doctors, we ought to attempt an answer to the question. I am not aware of any similar case of poisoning by this method in the literature, but another case of alleged poisoning via the ears is of interest. Ambroise Paré was wrongfully accused of murdering Francis II of France by blowing a poisonous powder into his ear. [1] Marlowe refers to this method of poisoning as one of the refined Italian variations with which he professed to be acquainted:

> *Lightborn.* You shall not need to give instructions;
> 'Tis not the first time I have kill'd a man;
> I learn'd in Naples how to poison flowers;
> To strangle with a lawn thrust down the throat;
> To pierce the wind pipe with a needle's point;
> Or, whilst one is asleep, to take a quill,
> And blow a little powder in his ears;
> Or open his mouth, and pour quick-silver down.
>
> *Edward the Second.*

To doctors the death raises such questions as:

(a) Could drops be poured into the ear without waking up the sleeping victim?
(b) What poison was used?
(c) How did it act?
(d) What was the cause of death?

Answers to all these questions, I hope to show, can be given from the evidence in the play.

(a) Could drops be poured into the ear without waking up the sleeping victim?

When one considers how sensitive the ear is, it is difficult to imagine that drops could be poured into it, even when the victim is asleep, without disturbing and wakening him. Yet that is precisely what we are asked to believe. The Ghost tells us what happened.

[1] Robert, M., *Les empoisonnements criminels au XVI siècle*. Thèse de Lyon, 1903.

> Sleeping within my orchard,
> My custom always of the afternoon,
> Upon my secure hour thy uncle stole,
> With juice of cursed hebona in a vial,
> And in the porches of my ears did pour
> The leperous distilment.
>
> 1, 5, 59-64.

Later in the play Hamlet tells us:

> 'A took my father grossly, full of bread
>
> III, 3, 80.

Now I imagine that the king had retired to the orchard to sleep off the effects of a hearty lunch. It is obvious that the weather must have been suitable. I picture a warm sultry afternoon with the old king asleep in the shade of an apple-tree. Next, it was 'upon my secure hour', i.e. when his sleep was soundest. If we are correct in our picture of a warm afternoon with a man sound asleep after a hearty meal, we may assume that Claudius, clutching the precious vial of poison in his hand, had thus warmed the already warm drops almost to blood temperature. And there are two comments about those drops which must be noted: they were 'the juice of cursed hebona', and they were a 'distilment'. The 'juice' suggests to me, pharmaceutically speaking, the expression of the essential oils of a plant; and 'distilment' further suggests that it was an alcoholic distillation of the essential oils, so beloved of the ancient alchemists. Let us suppose, therefore, that it was an oily, alcoholic fluid, warmed to body temperature, that was used. It seems not unreasonable to me to assume that drops such as these could be poured into the porches of the ears without disturbing a man who was deeply asleep.

(b) What poison was used?

This is an awkward question. We are told that it was the 'juice of cursed hebona'. Here a dispute arises among the experts on the text of the play. It is 'hebenon' in the folio edition but in the quarto edition it reads 'hebona'. In the literature these two words have been argued by the authorities on the subject to refer to henbane (hyoscyamus), ebony (guaiacum), hemlock (conium maculatum), deadly nightshade, crude oil of tobacco and the active principle of the yew tree (Taxus baccata). [1] In deciding for myself on henbane I am not influenced, I confess, by the pros and cons of the textual experts, I think the medical evidence in the Ghost's speech decides the issue. The 'juice' means the expressed juice of a plant. It could, therefore, be the juice of henbane: but ebony, or guaiacum, is the resin of a tree. There is thus a considerable difference and the old alchemists would not use the term 'juice' loosely for two such distinctive products. Next, it was a 'distilment', and again the alchemists would distil henbane but not guaiacum. In addition, henbane in a fraction of a grain is a very potent poison whereas the medicinal dose of guaiacum is 5-15 grains. From our study, too, of the accurate use to which Shakespeare put his knowledge of other poisons, it would be unlike our experience of him to find him tripping up in this important detail.

Henbane is the plant Hyoscyamus niger. It proves deadly when eaten by poultry, hence its old name. The poisonous alkaloid, Hyoscine, can be obtained both from the freshly expressed juice and from alcoholic extracts. A very small amount of this alkaloid can be fatal to human beings. While I know of no reference in the modern literature of toxicology to hyoscine being absorbed through the skin, we are not in a position to say precisely what preparation might have been used. But we do know that Pliny refers to oil of henbane in the treatment of earache. He warns that the use of this oil may cause mental disorder:

[1] Macht, Johns Hopkins Hospital Bulletin (1918), XXIX, 329, 165-170.

10

'oleum fit ex semine (hyoscyami) quod ipsum auribus
infusum temptat mentem'

(Nat. Hist., XXV, 4, 17).

Holland's translation of Pliny appeared just about the date of
the first quarto edition of Hamlet. Shakespeare, who was
well versed in the medical thought of his day, despite his 'little
Latin and less Greek', may have known of this reference.

(c) How did the poison act?

Gray had a method of anaesthetising the meatus and the ear
drum by drops which contained cocaine, rectified spirit and
anilin. [1]   But he warned against allowing these drops to
remain in the ear for more than ten minutes. The danger is
that the anilin may be absorbed through the skin of the meatus
and the ear drum and thus cause the formation of methaemo-
globin. Sir St. Clair Thomson reported a case in which he
used anilin in the treatment of a boil in the meatus. [2]   The
patient turned a distressingly deep blue colour but eventually
recovered. If this be true of anilin, can we accept that such a
mixture as I have suggested, an oily, alcoholic extract of
hyoscyamus—the 'juice of cursed hebona'—this 'leperous
distilment'—could be absorbed and exert a deadly poisonous
effect?

Macht has shown that a number of poisons can be and are
absorbed through the intact ear. [3]   He showed that the
powerful alkaloid, aconitin, was found to be absorbed through
the intact ears of animals even when introduced in an aqueous
solution. He found that the alkaloid nicotine was absorbed
equally rapidly through the ear. An alcoholic solution of the
belladonna alkaloids in the form of a weak tincture gave
positive experimental proof of the absorption of that drug as
shown by the paralysis of the vague terminals in the heart.

[1] Gray, Albert A., The Ear and its Diseases (1910), 112-113.
[2] British Medical Journal (1901), I, 957.
[3] Macht, Bulletin of the History of Medicine (1949), XXIII, 2.

Hyoscyamus in the form of an oil or a tincture had long been employed for the relief of earache; a compound tincture of hyoscyamus under the name of Balsamum tranquillans is official in several European pharmacopoeias.

If we do accept the possibility of this method of absorption of the poison, have we any means of answering the next question:

(d) What was the cause of death?

Shakespeare's description of the action of the poison may not be scientifically accurate but it is surely the most vivid and poetical description in the whole of toxicology. He tells of the leperous distilment:

> whose effect
> Holds such an enmity with blood of man
> That swift as quicksilver it courses through
> The natural gates and alleys of the body;
> And with a sudden vigour it doth posset
> And curd, like eager droppings into milk,
> The thin and wholesome blood. So did it mine.
>
> I, 5, 64-70.

In a recent article Macht has shown that those drugs which come under consideration in connection with the ear drops used in this play, namely, hyoscyamus, belladonna, conium and aconite, all produced marked shortening of the coagulation time of the blood. Other substances used as controls did not produce this effect.

But even yet Shakespeare has not finished with the details. His final description tells us clearly of the skin eruption which spread rapidly all over the victim's body as a result of the poisoning:

> And a most instant tetter bark'd about,
> Most lazar-like, with vile and loathsome crust,
> All my smooth body.
>
> I, 5, 71-73.

In Shakespeare's day, the word 'tetter' meant, in a comprehensive way, a skin disease. The drugs under consideration have given rise to various types of skin eruption but I would hazard a guess that the description here refers probably to an acute exfoliative dermatitis. This condition we know can be caused by small doses of poison in the blood, e.g. arsenic, and it can prove rapidly fatal. But I agree with Macht that 'Shakespeare's simile must be taken merely as a forcible poetic description of the rapid paralysis of respiration and circulation produced by the poison used'—whatever that poison may have been.

One further point intrigues me about this method of poisoning—there would be no external evidence to suggest that a crime had been committed. The 'leperous distilment' was probably a brownish oily extract and small in quantity— 'in a vial'. So even if the ears were examined after death, I doubt if the poison would be distinguishable from the soft wax of the ear.

There is, in fact, no suspicion of murder in the play until the Ghost's speech. The Ghost protests:

> 'Tis given out that, sleeping in my orchard,
> A serpent stung me; so the whole ear of Denmark
> Is by a forged process of my death
> Rankly abus'd.
>
> I, 5, 35-38.

It would seem, therefore, that here we have the almost perfect crime. No clues were left and death was attributed to the serpent's bite, as it might well have been. No suspicion was aroused in the minds of the people. We are left to decide on the evidence supplied by the Ghost. Shakespeare almost produced the perfect crime—if it had not been for that Ghost!

DID LADY MACBETH REALLY FAINT?

A. C. Bradley raised this question, and it may be put fairly to any writer on the medical aspects of Shakespeare's plays.

I feel it is a purely academic question because the answer to it does not influence in any way either the acting or the course of the play, nor does it materially affect our opinion of Lady Macbeth's character. But since it has been raised, the consideration of the problem in its medical aspects may be of interest. In the script of the scene (*II*, 3) in which the incident occurs, Shakespeare gives neither indication nor stage direction to tell us what he himself thought. It occurs when Macbeth is explaining to Banquo, Malcolm, Macduff and Donalbain why he killed the King's attendants:

> *Macbeth.* O, yet I do repent me of my fury
> That I did kill them.
>
> *Macduff.* Wherefore did you so?
>
> *Macbeth.* Who can be wise, amaz'd, temp'rate,
> and furious,
> Loyal and neutral, in a moment? No man.
> The expedition of my violent love
> Outrun the pauser reason. Here lay Duncan,
> His silver skin lac'd with his golden blood;
> And his gash'd stabs look'd like a breach in nature
> For ruin's wasteful entrance: there, the murderers,
> Steep'd in the colours of their trade, their daggers
> Unmannerly breech'd with gore. Who could refrain
> That had a heart to love, and in that heart
> Courage to make's love known?
>
> *Lady Macbeth.* Help me hence, ho!
>
> *Macduff.* Look to the lady.
>
> *Malcolm.* [*Aside to Donalbain*] Why do we hold out tongues that most may claim this argument for ours?
>
> *Donalbain.* [*Aside to Malcolm*] What should be spoken
> Here, where our fate, hid in an auger-hole,
> May rush and seize us? Let's away,
> Our tears are not yet brew'd.
>
> *Malcolm.* [*Aside to Donalbain*] Nor our strong sorrow
> Upon the foot of motion.
>
> *Banquo.* Look to the lady.
>
> [*Lady Macbeth is carried out.*

Malcolm and Donalbain were not apparently upset about Lady Macbeth's 'turn'; they were either not impressed by it or they were no gentlemen, for they continued to discuss their fears. Macduff and Banquo seemed a little concerned about her, so the witnesses present would appear to be equally divided. But the next moment both Malcolm and Donalbain agree with Macduff and Banquo about the insincerity of Macbeth and Lady Macbeth.

> *Malcolm.* What will you do? Let's not consort
> with them.
> To show an unfelt sorrow is an office
> Which the false man does easy.

And, of course, the false woman, too!
Macbeth makes no comment about his wife's distress, nor do the others present refer to it afterwards.
What of Lady Macbeth herself? Was she the fainting and wilting type? What do we know of her from the play up to this scene? When we meet her for the first time she is reading a letter from Macbeth in which he tells her of his meeting with the witches and of their prophecy that he would become King. He ends,

> This have I thought good to deliver thee, my dearest partner of greatness, that thou mightst not lose the dues of rejoicing by being ignorant of what greatness is promis'd thee. Lay it to thy heart, and farewell.
>
> I, 5.

This news would be heady wine to any woman. To Lady Macbeth's cool and calculating mind it is enough to set in motion the complete scheme of the subsequent tragedy. Woman-like, she understands her husband's mental make-up minutely.

> *Lady Macbeth.* Yet I do fear thy nature;
> It is too full o' the milk of human kindness
> To catch the nearest way. Thou wouldst be great;

Art not without ambition, but without
The illness should attend it. What thou wouldst highly,
That wouldst thou holily; wouldst not play false,
And yet wouldst wrongly win.

The word 'illness' here refers to 'evil or wickedness' (G. T. Onions), or 'ruthlessness' (Peter Alexander).

But she is quite certain that she can infuse Macbeth with the necessary ruthlessness to achieve his ambition and by the short cut upon which she has apparently already made up her mind.

> *Lady Macbeth.* Hie thee hither,
> That I may pour my spirits in thine ear,
> And chastise with the valour of my tongue
> All that impedes thee from the golden round
> Which fate and metaphysical aid doth seem
> To have thee crown'd withal.

No sooner has she decided her course of action than the messenger arrives to announce that Duncan, the King, will spend the night in her castle. She shows not the slightest hesitation.

> *Lady Macbeth.* The raven himself is hoarse
> That croaks the fatal entrance of Duncan
> Under my battlements. Come, you spirits
> That tend on mortal thoughts, unsex me here;
> And fill me, from the crown to the toe, top-full
> Of direst cruelty. Make thick my blood,
> Stop up th' access and passage to remorse,
> That no compunctions visitings of nature
> Shake my fell purpose nor keep peace between
> Th' effect and it. Come to my woman's breasts,
> And take my milk for gall, you murd'ring ministers,
> Wherever in your sightless substances
> You wait on nature's mischief. Come, thick night,
> And pall thee in the dunnest smoke of hell,
> That my keen knife see not the wound it makes,
> Nor heaven peep through the blanket of the dark
> To cry 'Hold, hold'.
>
> I, 5, 35-51

There is little doubt that had that speech in that particular moment of the play been written by anyone other than Shakespeare, it would have been changed to roaring melodrama. Instead, containing as it does some of the most inspired tragic poetry that Shakespeare ever wrote, it would convey to an Elizabethan audience not only the impending and inevitable tragedy but also that, although Lady Macbeth was going to act as an unsexed monster, that secret would be shared only between the audience and Lady Macbeth. The rest of the players would still see her as a woman and would expect her to act as one. This point becomes important when we come to the question of the fainting.

Macbeth arrives immediately after this speech and at once Lady Macbeth starts impatiently to work on him.

> *Lady Macbeth.* Thy letters have transported me beyond
> This ignorant present, and I feel now
> The future in the instant.

Macbeth innocently tells her that Duncan proposes to leave the following day. But Lady Macbeth has already taken command of the situation and of Macbeth.

> *Lady Macbeth.* O, never
> Shall sun that morrow see!
> Your face, my thane, is as a book where men
> May read strange matters. To beguile the time,
> Look like the time; bear welcome in your eye,
> Your hand, your tongue; look like th' innocent flower,
> But be the serpent under't. He that's coming
> Must be provided for; and you shall put
> This night's great business into my dispatch.
>
> I, 5, 57-65.

Her reception of the king is all that could be expected from a loyal subject and the hostess of the castle; she bore welcome in her eye, her hand, her tongue. No outward sign is given to the king or his entourage of the serpent in her mind:

> There's no art
> To find the mind's construction in the face.
>
> I, 4, 12-13.

But in the next scene when she seeks out Macbeth, who has left the banquet to soliloquise, and he tells her

> We will proceed no further in this business.
>
> I, 7, 31.

she turns on him in scorn and fury and scourges him with the live scorpions in her tongue. Any man, however strong-willed, would wilt under such an onslaught. And then comes the evidence that she meant what she said when she asked to be unsexed:

> *Lady Macbeth.* I have given suck, and know
> How tender 'tis to love the babe that milks me—
> I would, while it was smiling in my face,
> Have pluck'd my nipple from his boneless gums,
> And dash'd the brains out, had I so sworn,
> As you have done to this.

And at that moment we can accept that she would indeed have been as good as her word.

Having thus reduced Macbeth's martial bearing to mere putty in her hands, she begins once more to mould him to her will. Macbeth gives up the unequal contest:

> *Macbeth.* Bring forth men-children only;
> For thy undaunted mettle should compose
> Nothing but males.

But he is still doubtful if her scheme will work and be accepted as she plans.

> *Macbeth.* Will it not be receiv'd,
> When we have mark'd with blood those sleepy two
> Of his own chamber, and us'd their very daggers,
> That they have done't?

Her answer is, I think, the hint of how we should accept the fainting scene.

> *Lady Macbeth.* Who dares receive it other,
> As we shall make our griefs and clamour roar
> Upon his death?

Macbeth is re-assured and, as if to underline what is meant by the 'fainting', he ends the scene:

> False face must hide what the false heart doth know.

Now we come to the 'fainting' scene, but we must read it again in the light of the points already made. First, we have noted Lady Macbeth's determined ruthlessness:

> That I may pour my spirits in thine ear,
> And chastise with the valour of my tongue
> All that impedes thee from the golden round.

Next, her blatant appeal to be quite unfeminine:

> Unsex me here;
> And fill me, from the crown to the toe, top-full
> Of direst cruelty.
> . . . .
> Come, thick night,
> And pall thee in the dunnest smoke of hell,
> That my keen knife see not the wound it makes.

It is very rare in the annals of crime to find a woman using a knife as the instrument of murder, or even considering it. It is still more rare to find a knife used by a woman in suicide. When a knife is used, or contemplated, it can be fairly assumed that the woman has really been unsexed and will stop at nothing to achieve her purpose. Lady Macbeth certainly shows that degree of determination. Then, if her capacity for going to any length were doubted, we have her speech to Macbeth—'I have given suck, etc.'; and next her reassurance to Macbeth when he doubts how the crime will be received.

If now we re-read the scene at the actual point of the fainting, can we really believe that this woman, who, up to now, has shown no evidence of being the wilting type of female—indeed, quite the reverse—will faint at the mere description of the murdered, old king?

> Here lay Duncan,
> His silver skin lac'd with his golden blood.

Her faint comes at the point where it would be expected to emphasise Macbeth's apparently genuine emotion in his excuse for murdering the attendants, Malcolm was certainly not convinced by the exhibition.

> Let's not consort with them.
> To show an unfelt sorrow is an office
> Which the false man does easy.

He believed, as I do, that Lady Macbeth's 'faint' was a feint.

Chapter Eight

SHAKESPEARE'S MEDICAL APHORISMS

And here is the gnomic Shakespeare whose precepts have
delighted the generations with their moral prudence, whether
it comes from the youthful and sententious Valentine, with his

Home-keeping youth have ever homely wits

or in the more familiar and proverbial wisdom of Launce's

Blessing of your heart you brew good ale.

(Peter Alexander, *Shakespeare's Life and Art*, p. 73).

Why, Faustus, hast thou not attain'd that end?
Is not thy common talk found aphorisms?

Christopher Marlowe, *Doctor Faustus*.

MUCH of the clinical teaching of medicine can be
expressed in aphorisms, and these short, pithy maxims
are the crystallisation of long experience. They fall
becomingly from the lips of the fathers of medicine, and if
students are wise they will treasure them.

Of all the plays of Shakespeare's contemporaries that I have
read for comparison, not one has produced any medical
aphorisms worth recording. There is, indeed, only one
aphorism with which it is possible to make an analogy in
Shakespeare, viz.:

Give sorrow words. The grief that does not speak
Whispers the o'erfraught heart and bids it break.

Macbeth, IV, 3, 209-210.

Webster in *The White Devil* (II, 1, 276-277) expresses a similar
maxim:

Unkindness, do thy office; poor heart break:
Those are the killing griefs which dare not speak.

There are about fifty medical aphorisms to be found in

Shakespeare.   He was obviously interested in appetite and digestion for he refers to them frequently.

> Unquiet meals make ill digestions.
>
> *C. of E.*, V, i, 74.

> Fat paunches have lean pates; and dainty bits
> Make rich the ribs, but bankrup quite the wits.
>
> *L. L. L.*, I, 1, 26-27.

> Say, can you fast? Your stomachs are too young,
> And abstinence engenders maladies.
>
> *L.L.L.*, IV., 3, 200-291.

> a surfeit of the sweetest things
> The deepest loathing to the stomach brings.
>
> *M.N.D.*, II, 2, 137-138.

They are as sick that surfeit with too much, as they that starve with nothing. It is no mean happiness, therefore, to be seated in the mean: superfluity comes sooner by white hairs; but competency lives longer.

> *M. of V.*, I, 2, 5-9.

> Things sweet to taste prove in digestion sour.
>
> *R. II*, 1, 3, 236.

> As the last taste of sweets, is sweetest last,
> Writ in remembrance more than things long past.
>
> *R. II*, II, 1, 13-14.

> He tires betimes that spurs too fast betimes;
> With eager feeding food doth choke the feeder.
>
> *R. II*, II, 1, 36-37.

> And who abstains from meat that is not gaunt?
> For sleeping England long time have I watch'd;
> Watching breeds leanness, leanness is all gaunt.
>
> *R. II*, II, 1, 76-78.

> The sweetest honey
> Is loathsome in his own deliciousness,
> And in the taste confounds the appetite.
>
> *R. & J.*, II, 6, 11-13.

> Now good digestion wait on appetite,
> And health on both!
>
> *Mac.*, III, 4, 38-39.

> Like as, to make our appetite more keen,
> With eager compounds we our palate urge;
> As, to prevent our maladies unseen
> We sicken to shun sickness when we purge.
>
> *Sonnet,* 118.

> So surfeit-taking Tarquin fares this night:
> His taste delicious, in digestion souring,
> Devours his will, that lived by foul devouring.
>
> *Rape of Lucrece, v,* 100.

Shakespeare may have been recording a personal feeling, but he was also noting a fact for a great many men, when he wrote:

> There's no time for a man to recover his hair that grows bald by nature.
>
> *C. of E.,* II, 2, 71.

The fashionable Melancholia of his day is the subject of some of his aphorisms.

> Melancholy is the nurse of frenzy.
>
> *Shrew, Induc.,* 2, 130.

> A heavy heart bears not a nimble tongue.
>
> *L. L. L.,* V, 2, 725.

> The miserable have no other medicine
> But only hope.
>
> *M. for M.,* III, 1, 2-3.

> Life is as tedious as a twice-told tale
> Vexing the dull ear of a drowsy man.
>
> *K. John,* III, 4, 108-109.

About the gentle sex he is deeply informed.

> The venom clamours of a jealous woman
> Poisons more deadly than a mad dog's tooth.
>
> *C. of E.,* V, 1, 69-70.

It is not politic in the commonwealth of nature to preserve virginity. Loss of virginity is rational increase; and there was never virgin got till virginity was first lost.

> *All's Well,* I, 1, 121-124.

Younger than she are happy mothers made.
And too soon marr'd are those so early made.

R. & J., I, 2, 12-13.

Wounds were common enough amongst the robust Elizabethans and reference to them came naturally into their
everyday talk.

Scratch thee but with a pin, and there remains
Some scar of it.

A. Y. L., III, 5, 21-22.

He jests at scars that never felt a wound.

R. & J., II, 2, 1.

How poor are they that have not patience!
What wound did ever heal but by degrees?

Oth., II, 3, 358-359.

Those wounds heal ill that men do give themselves.

T. & C., III, 3, 229.

A patient's symptoms may colour his outlook on life.
Shakespeare knew this well.

He that is giddy thinks the world turns round.

Shrew, V, 2, 20.

Home-keeping youth have ever homely wits.

Two Gent., I, 1, 2.

You should hear reason.
And when I have heard it, what blessing brings it?
If not a present remedy, at least a patient sufferance.

Much Ado, I, 3, 5-7.

For there was never yet philosopher
That could endure the toothache patiently,
However they have writ the style of gods,
And made a push at chance and sufferance.

Much Ado, V, 1, 35-38.

Tut, man, one fire burns out another's burning.
One pain is lessen'd by another's anguish;
Turn giddy, and be holp by backward turning;
One desperate grief cures with another's languish:
Take thou some new infection to thy eye,
And the rank poison of the old will die.

R. & J., I, 2, 45-50.

But where the greater malady is fix'd
The lesser is scarce felt.

Lear, III, 4, 8-9.

Present fears
Are less than horrible imaginings.

Mac., I, 3, 137-138.

For pleasure and revenge
Have ears more deaf than adders to the voice
Of any true decision.

T. & C., II, 2, 171-173.

The remaining aphorisms illustrate the wide and constant background of medical affairs of everyday life which keep on recurring in Shakespeare's mind.

The brain may devise laws for the blood, but a hot temper leaps o'er a cold decree; such a hare is madness the youth, to skip o'er the meshes of good counsel the cripple.

M. of V., I, 2, 18-21.

A good wit will make use of anything. I will turn diseases to commodity.

2 *H. IV*, I, 2, 238-239.

'Tis a physic
That's bitter to sweet end.

M. for M., IV, 6, 7-8.

And falsehood falsehood cures, as fire cools fire
Within the scorched veins of one new-burn'd.

K. John, III, 1, 277-278.

Before the curing of a strong disease,
Even in the instant of repair and health,
The fit is strongest.

K. John, III, 4, 112-114.

Let's purge this choler without letting blood—
This we prescribe, though no physician;
Deep malice makes too deep incision.

R. II, I, 1, 153-155.

In poison there is physic.

2 *H. IV*, I, 1, 137.

> Diseases desperate grown
> By desperate appliances are relieved,
> Or not at all.
>
> *Ham.*, IV, 3, 9-11.

Thy bones are hollow; impiety has made a feast of thee.

> *M. for M.*, I, 2, 55.

> Care keeps his watch in every old man's eye,
> And where care lodges sleep will never lie;
> But where unbruised youth with unstuff'd brain
> Doth couch his limbs, there golden sleep doth reign.
>
> *R. & J.*, II, 3, 35-38.

> How oft when men are at the point of death
> Have they been merry! Which their keepers call
> A lightning before death.
>
> *R. & J.*, V, 3, 88-90.

> Our foster-nurse of nature is repose.
>
> *Lear*, IV, 4, 12.

> There's no art
> To find the mind's construction in the face.
>
> *Mac.*, I, 4, 11-12.

My favourite aphorism, however, is the shortest. In four words it defines the entire conception of Reflex Action and the Conditioned Reflexes.

> Mine eyes smell onions.
>
> *All's Well*, V, 3, 314.

And for all those doctor's who delude themselves by saying, 'It can't happen to me!' Shakespeare has a word of advice:

> By medicine life may be prolong'd, yet death
> Will seize the doctor too.
>
> *Cymb.*, V, 5, 29-30.

Chapter Nine

SHAKESPEARE'S CLINICAL DESCRIPTIONS

NO aspect of the study of Shakespeare shows more clearly his inspired poetic eye and mind, though not those of a doctor, than the clinical descriptions to be found in his writings. The accuracy of his observation, his apt use of words, and the clinical picture he leaves in the mind of his audience, or his reader, are not only unsurpassed, they are not even approached in clinical value in any medical writings, however erudite. Here, indeed, is a large part of the Art of Medicine, written for us by a layman. One instance, had there been no other, is enough to show the incalculable value his writing holds for us.

> All the world's a stage,
> And all the men and women merely players;
> They have their exits and their entrances;
> And one man in his time plays many parts,
> His acts being seven ages. At first the infant,
> Mewling and puking in the nurse's arms;
> Then the whining school-boy, with his satchel
> And shining morning face, creeping like snail
> Unwillingly to school. And then the lover,
> Sighing like furnace, with a woeful ballad
> Made to his mistress' eyebrow. Then a soldier,
> Full of strange oaths, and bearded like the pard,
> Jealous in honour, sudden and quick in quarrel,
> Seeking the bubble reputation
> Even in the cannon's mouth. And then the justice,
> In fair round belly with good capon lin'd,
> With eyes severe and beard of formal cut,
> Full of wise saws and modern instances;
> And so he plays his part. The sixth age shifts
> Into the lean and slipper'd pantaloon,
> With spectacles on nose and pouch on side,

His youthful hose, well sav'd, a world too wide
For his shrunk shank; and his big manly voice,
Turning again toward childish treble, pipes
And whistles in his sound. Last scene of all,
That ends this strange eventful history,
Is second childishness and mere oblivion;
Sans teeth, sans eyes, sans taste, sans every thing.
                              A. Y. L., II, 7, 139-166.

In that lies the epitome of all comment on the natural history
of man, as a doctor sees him.

Or consider the philosophy of life proper to a doctor in
his approach to his patients:

Be absolute for death; either death or life
Shall thereby be the sweeter. Reason thus with life.
If I do lose thee, I do lose a thing
That none but fools would keep. A breath thou art,
Servile to all the skyey influences,
That dost this habitation where thou keep'st
Hourly afflict. Merely, thou art Death's fool;
For him thou labour'st by thy flight to shun
And yet run'st toward him still. Thou art not noble;
For all th' accommodations that thou bear'st
Are nurs'd by baseness. Thou 'rt by no means valiant;
For thou dost fear the soft and tender fork
Of a poor worm. Thy best of rest is sleep,
And that thou oft provok'st; yet grossly fear'st
Thy death, which is no more. Thou art not thyself;
For thou exists on many a thousand grains
That issue out of dust. Happy thou art not;
For what thou hast not, still thou striv'st to get,
And what thou hast, forget'st. Thou art not certain;
For thy complexion shifts to strange effects,
After the moon. If thou art rich, thou'rt poor;
For, like an ass whose backs with ingots bows,
Thou bear'st thy heavy riches but a journey,
And Death unloads thee. Friend hast thou none;
For thine own bowels which do call thee sire,
The mere effusion of thy proper loins,
Do curse the gout, serpigo, and the rheum,

For ending thee no sooner. Thou hast nor youth nor age,
But, as it were, an after-dinner's sleep,
Dreaming on both; for all thy blessed youth
Becomes as aged, and doth beg the alms
Of palsied eld; and when thou art old and rich,
Thou hast neither heat, affection, limb, nor beauty,
To make thy riches pleasant. What's yet in this
That bears the name of life? Yet in this life
Lie hid moe thousand deaths; yet death we fear,
That makes these odds all even.

M. for M., III, 1, 5-41.

The picture of that serenity of mind is surely one that many a
doctor longs to meet in his patients—ideal advice, but how
seldom do we find the ideal patient to accept it!

The eternal revolt of youth against age, familiar enough
to all family doctors, is an attitude of mind which doctors
have to recall when dealing with the temperamental illnesses
of the adolescent. Gratiano states youth's attitude in terms of
medical interest.

                    Let me play the fool.
With mirth and laughter let old wrinkles come;
And let my liver rather heat with wine
Than my heart cool with mortifying groans.
Why should a man whose blood is warm within
Sit like his grandsire cut in alabaster,
Sleep when he wakes, and creep into the jaundice
By being peevish? I tell thee what, Antonio—
I love thee, and 'tis my love that speaks—
There are a sort of men whose visages
Do cream and mantle like a standing pond,
And do a wilful stillness entertain,
With purpose to be dress'd in an opinion
Of wisdom, gravity, profound conceit;
As who should say 'I am Sir Oracle,
And when I ope my lips let no dog bark'.
O my Antonio, I do know of these
That therefore only are reputed wise
For saying nothing; when, I am very sure

If they should speak, would almost damn those ears
Which, hearing them, would call their brothers fools.
                                        M. of V., I, 1, 79-99.

Shakespeare repeats the conception of creeping into the
jaundice by being peevish in *T. & C.*, I, 3, 1.

What grief hath set these jaundies o'er your cheeks?

It is interesting to note that Bucknill, as late as 1860, still
accepted that jaundice could be caused by what he calls a
'depressing emotion'.

This leads to the observation that Shakespeare's clinical
references are largely factual comments on diseases or are used
as realistic medical imagery. It is rare for him to make a
dissertation on the theoretical ideology of medical affairs
such as his contemporary dramatists loved to indulge in. For
example, nowhere in Shakespeare can be found the same
exposition of contemporary medical ideas, including humoral
pathology and astrology, as is found in Marlowe.

> *Tamburlaine.* Tell me what think you of my sickness
> now?
> *Physician.* I view'd your urine, and the hypostasis,
> Thick and obscure, doth make your danger great:
> Your veins are full of accidental heat,
> Whereby the moisture of your blood is dried:
> The humidum and calor, which some hold
> Is not a parcel of the elements,
> But of a substance more divine and pure,
> Is almost clean extinguished and spent;
> Which, being the cause of life, imports your death:
> Besides, my lord, this day is critical,
> Dangerous to those whose crisis is as yours:
> Your artiers, which alongst the veins convey
> The lively spirits which the heart engenders,
> Are parch'd and void of spirit, that the soul,
> Wanting those organons by which it moves,
> Cannot endure, by argument of art.

Yet, if your majesty may escape this day,
No doubt but you shall soon recover all.

    Tamburlaine.   Then will I comfort all my vital parts,
And live, in spite of death, above a day.

Tamburlaine the Great (Pt. 2), V, 3.

Shakespeare takes humoral pathology for granted and writes
more on observable facts, as seen, of course, by Shakespeare's
eye, and described as only his pen could.

The vividness of his description in the use of a disease is
well illustrated by the two ways in which he introduces
Epilepsy. In his day Epilepsy was the 'sacred' disease, the
victim being thought to be possessed of an evil spirit. The
epileptic attack was regarded with some awe and reverence.
Shakespeare first tries the effect of the description of an
epileptic attack on his audience. He describes how Caesar
refused the crown.

    Casca. And then he offered it the third time; he put it the
third time by; and still as he refus'd it, the rabblement hooted,
and clapp'd their chopt hands, and threw up their sweaty night-
caps, and uttered such a deal of stinking breath because Cæsar
refus'd the crown, that it had almost choked Cæsar; for he
swooned and fell down at it. And for mine own part I durst not
laugh, for fear of opening my lips and receiving the bad air.

    Cassius. But soft, I pray you. What, did Cæsar swoon?

    Casca. He fell down in the market-place, and foam'd at
mouth, and was speechless.

    Brutus. 'Tis very like. He hath the falling sickness.

. . . .

    Casca. When he came to himself again, he said, if he had
done or said anything amiss, he desir'd their worships to think
it was his infirmity. Three or four wenches, where I stood,
cried 'Alas, good soul!' and forgave him with all their hearts.
But there's no heed to be taken of them; if Cæsar had stabb'd
their mothers, they would have done no less.

Julius Cæsar, I, 2, 240-254: 269-274.

But in *Othello* he is bold enough to show the fit on the stage; he shows the mental confusion of the victim immediately preceding the fit. Othello falls, Cassio enters, and Iago explains what has happened.

> *Othello.* Lie with her—lie on her? We say lie on her when they belie her. Lie with her. Zounds, that's fulsome. Handkerchief—confessions—handkerchief! To confess, and be hang'd for his labour—first, to be hang'd, and then to confess. I tremble at it. Nature would not invest herself in such shadowing passion without some instruction. It is not words that shakes me thus—pish!—noses, ears, lips. Is't possible? Confess! Handkerchief! O devil!   [*Falls in a trance.*

> *Iago.* Work on,
> My medicine, work. Thus credulous fools are caught;
> And many worthy and chaste dames even thus,
> All guiltless, meet reproach. What, ho! my lord!
> My lord, I say! Othello!   [*Enter Cassio.*
>   How now, Cassio!

> *Cassio.* What's the matter?

> *Iago.* My lord is fall'n into an epilepsy.
> This is his second fit; he had one yesterday.

> *Cassio.* Rub him about the temples.

> *Iago.*   No, forbear.
> The lethargy must have his quiet course;
> If not, he foams at mouth, and by and by
> Breaks out to savage madness.

In both instances Shakespeare uses the epileptic attack at a most tense moment in the plays. In *Julius Caesar*, it is at the moment when Caesar has refused the crown for the third time: we may feel that he does so reluctantly, for Caesar was an ambitious man. In *Othello*, the attack appears just at that moment when Othello is at last persuaded of Desdemona's unfaithfulness. An Elizabethan audience would be much impressed by hearing about, and more so by actually seeing the 'sacred' disease. And at that particular point in both plays Shakespeare wanted to transfer the sympathy of his audience to the characters concerned, Caesar and Othello. The epileptic attack served admirably to increase the pathos of the impending and, by now, inevitable tragedies; it intensified the dramatic *denouement*. This use of a medical situation to enhance the dramatic effect is an absorbing theme, worth more detailed study.

It has been said that Shakespeare did not draw his women characters as real women. Considered medically, however, they are superb. If any young doctor has not yet met Constance, the prototype of the angry, over-anxious, excited and self-interested mother defending her child against all odds and all comers, then he should make the acquaintance of this character right away. And he can be assured that he will meet her modern descendants in real life very soon and very often. First, meet her as the widow releasing, in righteous wrath, a flood of pent-up emotion and self-pity.

> *Constance.* Thou shalt be punish'd for thus
> frightening me,
> For I am sick and capable of fears,
> Oppress'd with wrongs, and therefore full of fears;
> A widow, husbandless, subject to fears;
> A woman, naturally born to fears;
> And though thou now confess thou didst but jest,
> With my vex'd spirits I cannot take a truce,
> But they will quake and tremble all this day.
>
> *King John*, III, 1, 11-18.

Next, as she justified her tirade in defence of her son.

> *Arthur.* I do beseech you, madam, be content.
>
> *Constance.* If thou that bid'st me be content wert
> grim,
> Ugly, and sland'rous to thy mother's womb,
> Full of unpleasing blots and sightless stains,
> Lame, foolish, crooked, swart, prodigious,
> Patch'd with foul moles and eye-offending marks,
> I would not care, I then would be content;
> For then I should not love thee; no, nor thou

Become thy great birth, nor deserve a crown.
But thou art fair, and at thy birth, dear boy,
Nature and Fortune join'd to make thee great:
Of Nature's gifts thou mayst with lillies boast,
And with the half-blown rose.

King John, III, 1, 42-54.

Lastly, when she has heard her son is a prisoner; she refuses all consolation or appeasement and turns on the Cardinal.

> *Constance.*   And, father Cardinal, I have heard you
>   say
> That we shall see and know our friends in heaven;
> If that be true, I shall see my boy again;
> For since the birth of Cain, the first male child,
> To him that did but yesterday suspire,
> There was not such a gracious creature born.
> But now will canker sorrow eat my bud
> And chase the native beauty from his cheek,
> And he will look as hollow as a ghost,
> As dim and meagre as an ague's fit;
> And so he'll die; and, rising so again,
> When I shall meet him in the court of heaven
> I shall not know him.   Therefore never, never
> Must I behold my pretty Arthur more.

King John, III, 4, 76-89.

That is an excellent picture, clinically, of the distraught and unconsolable mother, but not unreasoning: she has lots of reasoned and logical argument.   The doctor's difficulty, as is the Cardinal's, is to counter her arguments and convince her!

Falstaff abounds in clinical material but this has been fully recorded in the chapter on the 'Medical History of Sir John Falstaff' and need no be repeated here.   The death of Falstaff is worthy of particular attention, especially, as I imagine, because it was a common mode of death in Elizabethan medicine; and, indeed, it may paradoxically and prophetically be an accurate description of Shakespeare's own death-bed scene.

One further death must be noted because of its medico-legal

importance—the death of Gloucester in 2 *H. VI*, III, 2. Here is an instance of how accurate Shakespeare could be not only in all his medical detail but also in the legal significance of that detail. He begins by describing the appearance of a person who has died a natural death, and then he contrasts that description with the appearance of the body of Gloucester, who has been strangled. In this speech every important medico-legal point in the evidence of strangulation is included. It might even be accepted in a court of law to-day as sufficient evidence of death by strangulation.

> *Warwick.*   See how the blood is settled in his face.
> Oft have I seen a timely-parted ghost,
> Of ashy semblance, meagre, pale, and bloodless,
> Being all descended to the labouring heart,
> Who, in the conflict that it holds with death,
> Attracts the same for aidance 'gainst the enemy,
> Which with the heart there cools, and ne'er returneth
> To blush and beautify the cheek again.
> But see, his face is black and full of blood;
> His eye-balls further out than when he liv'd,
> Staring full ghastly like a strangled man;
> His hair uprear'd, his nostrils stretch'd with struggling;
> His hands abroad display'd, as one that grasp'd
> And tugg'd for life, and was by strength subdu'd.
> Look, on the sheets his hair, you see, is sticking;
> His well-proportion'd beard made rough and rugged,
> Like to the summer's corn by tempest lodged.
> It cannot be but he was murd'red here:
> The least of all these signs were probable.

One clinical record of what must have been a common sight in Shakespeare's day and may have been made from his own daily observation is worth noting, if only because of its rarity to-day. It is the detailed description of the ravages of tertiary syphilis. But it has only become rare since the discovery of Penicillin. Recent as that discovery is, it is none the less true that medical students in this antibiotic era may not have seen such a case. This revolting and appalling picture may crop up occasionally even to-day in patients who have unfortunately escaped treatment. Shakespeare records all the awful results.

> Consumptions sow
> In hollow bones of man; strike their sharp shins,
> And mar men's spurring. Crack the lawyer's voice,
> That he may never more false title plead,
> Nor sound his quillets shrilly. Hoar the flamen,
> That scolds against the quality of flesh
> And not believes himself. Down with the nose,
> Down with it flat, take the bridge quite away
> Of him that, his particular to foresee,
> Smells from the general weal. Make curl'd-pate ruffians bald,
> And let the unscarr'd braggarts of the war
> Derive some pain from you. Plague all,
> That your activity may defeat and quell
> The source of all erection. There's more gold.
> Do you damn others, and let this dam you,
> And ditches grave you all!
>
> *Timon of Athens*, IV, 3, 150-165.

But it is in the short clinical flashes that we discover the medical value of Shakespeare's genius. In a very few words of poetic insight he can define for us, in terms undreamt of medically, whole pictures of medical conditions never before or since expressed so vividly. A few examples only need be noted here:

1. The break in the boy's voice at puberty.

> And speak between the change of man and boy
> With a reed voice; and turn two mincing steps
> Into a manly stride.
>
> *M. of V.*, III, 4, 66-68.

2. The love-sick maid.

> She never told her love,
> But let concealment, like a worm i' th' bud,
> Feed on her damask cheek. She pin'd in thought;
> And with a green and yellow melancholy
> She sat like Patience on a monument,
> Smiling at grief.
>
> *T. N.*, II, 4, 109-114.

3. Pregnancy.

> Your brother and his lover have embrac'd.
> As those that feed grow full, as blossoming time
> That from the seedness the bare fallow brings
> To teeming foison, even so her plenteous womb
> Expresseth his full tilth and husbandry.
>
> *M. for M.*, I, 4, 40-44.

> Great-bellied women,
> That had not half a week to go, like rams
> In the old time of war, would shake the press,
> And make 'em reel before 'em.
>
> *H. VIII*, IV, 1, 76-79.

4. Prognosis.

> Oft expectation fails, and most oft there
> Where most it promises; and of it hits
> Where hope is coldest, and despair most fits.
>
> *All's Well*, II, 1, 141-143.

5. Palpitation.

> I have tremor cordis on me; my heart dances.
>
> *Winter's Tale*, I, 2, 110.

6. The menses.

I'll warrant him for drowning, though the ship were no stronger
than a nutshell, and as leaky as an unstanched wench

> *The Tempest*, I, 1, 43-45.

7. Goitre and the hunch-back (Pott's disease).

> When we were boys,
> Who would believe that there were mountaineers,
> Dewlapp'd like bulls, whose throats had hanging at 'em
> Wallets of flesh? or that there were such men
> Whose heads stood in their breasts?
>
> *The Tempest*, III. 3, 43-47.

8. The ageing mind.

> And as with age his body uglier grows,
> So his mind cankers.
>
> *The Tempest*, IV, 1, 191-192.

9. Angina pectoris.

> To signify unto his Majesty
> That Cardinal Beaufort is at point of death;
> For suddenly a grievous sickness took him
> That makes him gasp, and stare, and catch the air.
>
> *2 H. VI*, III, 2, 368-371.

10. Fear.

> Cold fearful drops stand on my trembling flesh.
> What do I fear?
>
> *R. III*, V, 3, 181-182.

> I am surprised with an uncouth fear;
> A chilling sweat o'er-runs my trembling joints;
> My heart suspects more than mine eye can see.
>
> *Titus Andronicus*, II, 3, 212-213.

> I am Thane of Cawdor.
> If good, why do I yield to that suggestion
> Whose horrid image doth unfix my hair
> And make my seated heart knock at my ribs
> Against the use of nature? Present fears
> Are less than horrible imaginings.
>
> *Macbeth*, I, 3, 133-138.

11. The Menopause.

> Have we more sons? or are we like to have?
> Is not my teeming date drunk up with time?
>
> *R. II*, V, 2, 90-91.

12. Impending death.

> O Griffith, sick to death!
> My legs like loaden branches bow to th' earth,
> Willing to leave their burden.
>
> *H. VIII*, IV, 2, 2-4.

> Do you note
> How much her Grace is alter'd on the sudden?
> How long her face is drawn! How pale she looks,
> And of an earthly cold! Mark her eyes.
>
> She is going, wench. Pray, pray.
>
> *H. VIII*, IV, 2, 95-99.

13. Loss of weight.

Bardolph, am I not fall'n away vilely since this last action? Do
I not bate? Do I not dwindle? Why, my skin hangs about me
like an old lady's loose gown; I am withered like an old applejohn.

2 H. IV, III, 3, 1-4.

Sometimes he uses a single word, a simple adjective, which
never appears in medical descriptions, but which does express
completely what we try to say at great length. An example
is the use of the adjective 'embossed'. In medical literature
when we write about a carbuncle or an ulcer, usually we describe it as having a 'heaped-up' or 'rolled-over' edge. Shakespeare does it much more aptly.

> And all th' embossed sores and headed evils
> That thou with license of free foot hast caught
> Wouldst thou disgorge into the general world.
>
> As You Like It, II, 7, 67-69.

> But yet thou art my flesh, my blood, my daughter;
> Or rather a disease that's in my flesh,
> Which I must needs call mine; thou art a boil,
> A plague-sore, or embossed carbuncle
> In my corrupted blood.
>
> Lear, II, 4, 220-224.

Many of his clinical descriptions are, of course, folk-lore in
pattern, and of a type which still persists among our patients.
How many new young mothers still see every detail of their
husband's face in their new-born baby?

> It is yours.
> And, might we lay th' old proverb to your charge,
> So like you 'tis the worse. Behold, my lords,
> Although the print be little, the whole matter
> And copy of the father—eye, nose, lip,
> The trick of's frown, his forehead; nay, the valley,
> The pretty dimples of his chin and cheek; his smiles;
> The very mould and frame of hand, nail, finger.
> And thou, good goddess Nature, which hast made it

So like to him that got it, if thou hast
The ordering of the mind too, 'mongst all colours
No yellow in't, lest she suspect, as he does,
Her children not her husband's!

The Winter's Tale, II, 3, 95-107.

It was recognised in Elizabethan times, just as well as it is by
the modern clinician, that the appearance of the eyes gives
some impression of the patient's condition in a general way.
It was then as it is now a clinical impression, indefinable almost,
but very helpful. This was the kind of clinical sign which
Shakespeare could not fail to observe and record. In this sense,
he mentions eyes frequently; whereas his contemporary
dramatists, in the plays I have referred to write about eyes,
clinically, on only two occasions—once in *Volpone*, I, 1.

How does his apoplex?
Is that strong on him still?

Most violent.
His speech is broken, and his eyes are set,
His face drawn longer that 'twas wont—

. . . .
His mount
Is ever gaping, and his eyelids hang.

. . . .
A freezing numbness stiffens all his joints,
And makes the colour of his flesh like lead.

. . . .
His pulse beats slow, and dull

. . . .
And from his brain—
Flows a cold sweat, with a continual rheum
Forth the resolved corners of his eyes.

and in *The Duchess of Malfi*, II, 1, referring to the change in
the face, which occurs in pregnancy:

I observe our duchess
Is sick a-days, she pukes, her stomach seethes,
The fins of her eye-lids look most teeming blue,
She wanes i' th' cheek, and waxes fat i' th' flank.

Contrast these with Shakespeare's clinical references to eyes:

> Methinks I see these things with parted eye,
> When every thing seems double.
>> *Midsummer Night's Dream*, IV, 1, 186-187.

> Beaufort's red sparkling eyes blab his heart's malice,
> And Suffolk's cloudy brow his stormy hate.
>> 2 *H. VI*, III, 1, 154-155.

> Uncle, even in the glasses of thine eyes
> I see thy grieved heart.
>> *R. II*, I, 3, 208-209.

> His eye is hollow, and he changes much.
>> 2 *H. IV*, IV, 5, 6.

> Do you note
> How much her Grace is alter'd on the sudden?
> How long her face is drawn! How pale she looks,
> And of an earthy cold! Mark her eyes.
> She is going, wench. Pray, pray.
>> *H. VIII*, IV, 2, 95-99.

His references to the eyes of old people are an essential part of particularly good pictures of old age.

> Do you set down your name in the scroll of youth, that are written down old with all the characters of age? Have you not a moist eye, a dry hand, a yellow cheek, a white beard, a decreasing leg, an increasing belly? Is not your voice broken, your wind short, your chin double, your wit single, and every part about you blasted with antiquity? And will you yet call yourself young? Fie, fie, fie, Sir John?
>> 2 *H. IV*, I, 2, 168-175.

> A good leg will fall; a straight back will stoop; a black beard will turn white; a curl'd pate will grow bald; a fair face will wither; a full eye will wax hollow. But a good heart, Kate, is the sun and the moon; or, rather, the sun, and not the moon— for it shines bright and never changes, but keeps his course truly.
>> *H. V*, V, 2, 158-163.

> Slanders, sir; for the satirical rogue says here that old men have grey beards; that their faces are wrinkled; their eyes purging thick amber and plum-tree gum; and that they have a plentiful lack of wit, together with most weak hams—all which, sir, though I most powerfully and potently believe, yet I hold it not

honesty to have it thus set down; for you yourself, sir, shall grow old as I am, if, like a crab, you could go backward.

Hamlet, II, 2, 195-202.

These extracts may serve as an indication of what the reader can expect to find should he approach the plays with a medical interest in the clinical sense. And to end this note about them, perhaps no finer scene has ever been written in its medical appeal than the death of King John. It leaves with the medical reader an indelible impression, an end though familiar enough to him yet here recorded so incomparably in the poetry of Shakespeare.

> *Prince.* It is too late; the life of all his blood
> Is touch'd corruptibly, and his pure brain,
> Which some suppose the soul's frail dwelling-house,
> Doth by the idle comments that it makes
> Foretell the ending of mortality.
>
> . . . .
>
> O vanity of sickness! Fierce extremes
> In their continuance will not feel themselves.
> Death, having prey'd upon the outward parts,
> Leaves them invisible, and his siege is now
> Against the mind, the which he pricks and wounds
> With many legions of strange fantasies,
> Which, in their throng and press to that last hold,
> Confound themselves. 'Tis strange that death should sing.
> I am the cygnet to this pale faint swan
> Who chants a doleful hymn to his own death,
> And from the organ-pipe of frailty sings
> His soul and body to their lasting rest.
>
> . . . .
>
>   *King.* Ay, marry, now my soul hath elbow-
>   room;
> It would not out at windows nor at doors.
> There is so hot a summer in my bosom
> That all my bowels crumble up to dust.
> I am a scribbled form drawn with a pen
> Upon a parchment, and against this fire
> Do I shrink up.   *King John*, V, 7.

1st Witch. Thrice the brinded cat hath mew'd.

2nd Witch. Thrice and once the hedge-pig whin'd.

3rd Witch. Harpies cries; 'tis time, 'tis time.

1st Witch. Round about the cauldron go;
In the poison'd entrails throw.
Toad that under cold stone
Days and nights has thirty-one
Swelt'red venom sleeping got
Boil thou first i' th' charmed pot.

All. Double, double toil and trouble;
Fire burn, and cauldron bubble.

2nd Witch Fillet of a fenny snake,
In the cauldron boil and bake;
Eye of newt, and toe of frog,
Wool of bat, and tongue of dog,
Adder's fork, and blind-worm's sting,
Lizard's leg, and howlet's wing—
For a charm of pow'rful trouble,
Like a hell-broth boil and bubble.

All. Double, double toil and trouble;
Fire burn, and cauldron bubble.

3rd Witch. Scale of dragon, tooth of wolf,
Witch's mummy, maw and gulf
Of the ravin'd salt-sea shark,
Root of hemlock digg'd i' th' dark,
Liver of blaspheming Jew,
Gall of goat, and slips of yew
Sliver'd in the moon's eclipse,
Nose of Turk, and Tartar's lips,
Finger of birth-strangled babe
Ditch-deliver'd by a drab—
Make the gruel thick and slab;
Add thereto a tiger's chaudron,
For th' ingredience of our cauldron.

All. Double, double toil and trouble;
Fire burn, and cauldron bubble.

2nd Witch. Cool it with a baboon's blood,
Then the charm is firm and good.

Macbeth, IV, 1, 1-38.

Chapter Ten

SHAKESPEARE ON DRUGS AND POISONS

AFTER considering the drugs and the methods of their preparation in the Elizabethan age and even later, up to the middle of the seventeenth century, the Witches' Brew may not be regarded so much the Devil's Hash as, however regretfully, something very near the medicine dispensed in that period to an ignorant and superstitious people who were prepared to swallow anything. It may, indeed, be found to resemble the *pot-au-feu* of the mediaeval alchemists. Many of the witches' ingredients were, in fact, used in the compounding of medicines in Shakespeare's day, and some are even recorded by his son-in-law, John Hall, in his *Select Observations*, years after Shakespeare's death. Hall believed in the efficacy of this type of pharmacy for he used something resembling it in the treatment of his own illness and in that of his wife, Shakespeare's daughter, Susanna, and also in that of his own daughter, Elizabeth. When he was 57, he had an illness which lasted from 27th August-29th September, 1632. The entire record of it need not be given but among other complaints he notes:

I also had Convulsion of the Mouth and Eyes. Then was a pigeon cut open alive, and applied to my feet, to draw down the Vapours; for I was often afflicted with a slight Delirium.

Observation LX (2nd Cent.).

In one illness of his wife's (*Observation XXXIII*), in which she was 'troubled with Scurvy, accompanied with Pain of the Loins, Corruption of the Gums, Stinking Breath, Melancholy, Wind, Cardiac Passion, Laziness, difficulty of Breathing, fear of the Mother, binding of the Belly, and torment there, and all of a long continuance, with restlessness and weakness', he records that the following were used in the course of her treatment:

Electuary of Tamarinds.   Cream of Tartar.

Emplastrum Oxycroceum.

Capon's Grease.   Oil of Sweet Almonds.

Macilage of the Roots of Althaea, drawn with Mallow Water.

Conserve of the tops and leaves of Scurvy Grass.

The flowers of Buglos, Clove Gilly-flowers and Damask Roses.

The flesh of Candid Nutmeg, Citron Pills.

Honey of Juniper Berries.   Syrup of Cinamon.   Oil of Sulphur.

Honey.   Cummin Seed.   Fumatory.   Brook-lime.

Water Cresses.   Betony.   Agrimony.   Harts-tongue.

Bark of Capparis, Ash,   Tamaris.

Roots of Elicampana.   Polipody.

Madder Liquoris.   Calamus Aromaticus.   Eringoes.

Yellow Sanders.   Red Coral.   Shavings of Ivory.

Cloves, Mace, Cinamon, Ginger.

Flowers of Broom, Rosemary, Marygolds, Epithymum.

Steel prepared according to Crato.   White Wine.   Saffron.

His treatment for a boy 'afflicted with the falling sickness' included:

First, I caused round pieces of Piony Roots to be hanged about the neck. When the Fit afflicted, I commanded to be applied with a spunge to the Nostrils, the Juyce of Rhue, mixed with White-wine Vinegar; by the use of which it was presently recovered; and falling into the fit again, it was removed in the same manner. . . . The hair was powdered with the powder of the Roots of Piony. And thus the child was delivered from all its Fits.

For the treatment of a child 'being miserably afflicted with a Feaver and Worms, so that Death was only expected', he used, among other things, an ointment 'mixed with Spiders Webs, and a little Powder of Nutshels'. This was applied 'to the Pulse'.

Though Shakespeare never mentions any of the revolting ingredients, except in the brew—certainly never as medicine for humans—his contemporaries refer to them as if they were part of the medicine of their daily life.

> *Corvino.*   I am curs'd,
> I am bewitch'd, my crosses meet to vex me.
> How? how? how? how?
>
> *Mosca.*   Why, sir, with Scoto's oil;
> Corbaccio and Voltore brought of it,
> Whilst I was busy in an inner room—
>
> . . . .
>
> *Corvino.*   All his ingredients
> Are a sheep's gall, a roasted bitch's marrow,
> Some few sod earwigs, pounded caterpillars,
> A little capon's grease, and fasting spittle:
> I know them to a dram.
>
> *Mosca.*   I know not, sir;
> But some on't, they pour'd into his ears,
> Some in his nostrils and recover'd him;
> Applying but the fricace.
>
> *Volpone*, II, 3.
>
> *Volpone.*   O, if you do love me,
> No more: I sweat, and suffer, at the mention
> Of any dream; feel how I tremble yet.
>
> *Lady Politick Would-be.*   Alas, good soul! the passion of
>   heart.
> Seed-pearl were good now, boil'd with syrup of apples,
> Tincture of gold, and coral, citron-pills,
> Your elicampane root, myrobalanes—
>
> *Volpone.* [*Aside*] Ah me, I have ta'en a grasshopper by
>   the wing!
>
> *Lady P.*   Burnt silk, and amber: You have muscadel
> Good in the house—
>
> *Volpone.*   You will not drink, and part?
>
> *Lady P.*   No, fear not that, I doubt, we shall not get
> Some English saffron, half a dram would serve;
> Your sixteen cloves, a little musk, dried mints,
> Bugloss, and barley-meal—

Volpone.   [*Aside*] She's in again!
Before I feign'd diseases, now I have one.

Lady P.   And these applied with a scarlet cloth.

Volpone.   [*Aside*] Another flood of words! a very torrent!

Lady P.   Shall I, sir, make you a poultice?

Volpone.   No, no, no,
I'm very well, you need prescribe no more.

Volpone, III, 2.

In the eleven plays of his contemporaries studied here for comparison, significant references to drugs and poisons occur three and a half times more frequently than in Shakespeare's plays. Shakespeare is cautious and correct in his use of drugs and poisons, whereas his contemporaries appear recklessly anxious to include such references, probably well aware of the popular appeal to an audience of any medical topic, especially if there was any suggestion of the miraculous about it. The medicines of Shakespeare's day were derived largely, though not exclusively, from herbs, and throughout the plays Shakespeare mentions 36 varieties of these herbs so used. But Shakespeare was aware that medicines were also derived from metals and minerals. Cerimon mentions the fact,

> the blest infusions,
> That dwell in vegetives, in metals, stones.

Pericles, III, 2, 35-36.

Marlowe had great faith in these.

Olympia.   An ointment which a cunning alchymist
Distilled from the purest balsamum
And simplest extracts of all minerals,
In which the essential form of marble stone,
Temper'd with science metaphysical,
And spells of magic from the mouths of spirits,
With which if you but 'noint your tender skin,
Nor pistol, sword, nor lance, can pierce your flesh.

Tamburlaine the Great, IV, 2.

In their crudity they were indeed
                    physic
            That's bitter to sweet end.

Measure for Measure, **IV, 6, 7-8.**

The method of collecting and preparing the medicines from herbs—a custom which still exists in some country districts—was well-known to the countryman, Shakespeare. Friar Lawrence describes it:

The gray-ey'd morn smiles on the frowning night,
Check'ring the eastern clouds with streaks of light;
And fleckel'd darkness like a drunkard reels
From forth day's path and Titan's fiery wheels.
Now, ere the sun advance his burning eye
The day to cheer and night's dank dew to dry,
I must up-fill this osier cage of ours
With baleful weeds and precious-juiced flowers.
The earth that's nature's mother is her tomb;
What is her burying grave, that is her womb.
And from her womb children of divers kind
We sucking on her natural bosom find;
Many for many virtues excellent,
None but for some, and yet all different.
O, mickle is the powerful grace that lies
In plants, herbs, stones, and their true qualities;
For nought so vile that on the earth doth live
But to the earth some special good doth give;
Nor aught so good but, strain'd from that fair use,
Revolts from true birth, stumbling on abuse:
Virtue itself turns vice, being misapplied,
And vice sometime's by action dignified.
Within the infant rind of this weak flower
Poison hath residence, and medicine power;
For this, being smelt, with that part cheers each part;
Being tasted, slays all senses with the heart.
Two such opposed kings encamp them still
In man as well as herbs—grace and rude will;
And where the worser is predominant,
Full soon the canker death eats up that plant.

R. & J., **II, 3, 1-30.**

The preparation of medicines from the herbs was part of the household duties in the great Elizabethan houses, and something of the dangers of this custom is found in *Cymbeline*.

> *Queen.* Whiles yet the dew's on the ground gather
> these flowers.
>
> . . . .
>
> Master Doctor, have you brought those drugs?
> *Cornelius.* Pleaseth your Highness, ay. Here they
> are, madam.
> But I beseech your Grace, without offence—
> My conscience bids me ask—wherefore you have
> Commanded of me these most poisonous compounds,
> Which are the movers of a languishing death,
> But, though slow, deadly?
>
> *Queen.*   I wonder, Doctor,
> Thou ask'st me such a question. Have I not been
> Thy pupil long? Hast thou not learn'd me how
> To make perfumes? distil? preserve? yea, so
> That our great king himself doth woo me oft
> For my confections? Having thus far proceeded—
> Unless thou think'st me devilish—is't not meet
> That I did amplify my judgment in
> Other conclusions? I will try the forces
> Of these thy compounds on such creatures as
> We count not worth the hanging—but none human—
> To try the vigour of them, and apply
> Allayments to their act, and by them gather
> Their several virtues and effects.
>
> *Cornelius.*   Your Highness
> Shall from this practice but make hard your heart;
> Besides, the seeing these effects will be
> Both noisome and infectious.
>
> *Queen.*   O, content thee.
>
> . . . .
>
> *Cornelius.* I do suspect you, madam;
> But you shall do no harm.
>
> . . . .
>
> I do not like her. She doth think she has
> Strange ling'ring poisons. I do know her spirit,

And will not trust one of her malice with
A drug of such damn'd nature. Those she has
Will stupefy and dull the sense awhile,
Which first perchance she'll prove on cats and dogs,
Then afterward up higher; but there is
No danger in what show of death it makes,
More than the locking up the spirits a time,
To be more fresh, reviving. She is fool'd
With a most false effect; and I the truer
So to be false with her.

Cymbeline, I, 5, 1-43.

Secret remedies were common in Shakespeare's time and
were closely kept by surgeons more frequently than by
physicians. But C. J. Sisson has found a court record about
one of the secret remedies of even the great William Harvey. [1]
Thus Shakespeare's audience would accept without question
that Helena's remedy for the King's fistula would do exactly
what she claimed for it.

Helena. You know my father left me some prescriptions
Of rare and prov'd effects, such as his reading
And manifest experience had collected
For general sovereignty; and that he will'd me
In heedfull'st reservation to bestow them,
As notes whose faculties inclusive were
More than they were in note. Amongst the rest
There is a remedy, approv'd, set down,
To cure the desperate languishings whereof
The King is render'd lost.

. . . .

Countess.   But think you, Helen,
If you should tender your supposed aid,
He would receive it? He and his physicians
Are of a mind: he, that they cannnot help him;
They, that they cannot help. How shall they credit
A poor unlearned virgin, when the schools,
Embowell'd of their doctrine, have left off
The danger to itself?

[1] Sisson, C. J., *The Listener*, 21 June, 1951.

Helena.   There's something in't
More than my father's skill, which was the great'st
Of his profession, that his good receipt
Shall for my legacy be sanctified
By th' luckiest stars in heaven; and, would your honour
But give me leave to try success, I'd venture
The well-lost life of mine on his Grace's cure
By such a day and hour.
                                        All's Well, I, 3, 212-221 : 225-240.

Helena.   On's bed of death
Many receipts he gave me; chiefly one,
Which, as the dearest issue of his practice,
And of his old experience th' only darling,
He bade me store up as a triple eye,
Safer than mine own two more dear. I have so
And, hearing your high Majesty is touch'd
With that malignant cause wherein the honour
Of my dear father's gift stands chief in power,
I come to tender it, and my appliance,
With all bound humbleness.

King.   We thank you, maiden;
But may not be so credulous of cure,
When our most learned doctors leave us, and
The congregated college have concluded
That labouring art can never ransom nature
From her inaidable estate—I say we must not
So stain our judgment, or corrupt our hope,
To prostitute our past-cure malady
To empirics; or to dissever so
Our great self and our credit to esteem
A senseless help, when help past sense we deem.
                                        All's Well, II, 1, 100-123.

King.   Plutus himself
That knows the tinct and multiplying med'cine,
Hath not in nature's mystery more science
Than I have in this ring.
                                        All's Well, V, 3, 101-104.

There are two drugs, mentioned by Shakespeare in the
tragedies, which raise medical problems. These problems are

discussed in the chapter on 'Medical Problems in the Tragedies'. The first drug is hebenon, the nature of which need not be discussed again here. The reference is unique in that Shake-speare describes what was, in his time, believed to be the action of the drug in the terms of the period. It is a most vivid and imaginative description.

> *Ghost.*   Sleeping within my orchard,
> My custom always of the afternoon,
> Upon my secure hour thy uncle stole,
> With juice of cursed hebenon in a vial,
> And in the porches of my ears did pour
> The leperous distilment; whose effect
> Holds such an enmity with blood of man
> That swift as quicksilver it courses through
> The natural gates and alleys of the body;
> And with a sudden vigour it doth posset
> And curd, like eager droppings into milk,
> The thin and wholesome blood. So did it mine;
> And a most instant tetter bar'd about,
> Most lazar-like, with vile and loathsome crust,
> All my smooth body.
>
>   *Hamlet*, I, 5, 59-73.

The other drug is the one given by Friar Lawrence to Juliet. The nature of this drug cannot even be guessed at but drugs of this imaginative nature were popular with Elizabethan audiences. Shakespeare does not enlighten us on his views about how the drug acts in this instance, but he gives a remark-able clinical picture of its effects. The result, to a medical mind, serves to heighten the pathos of the tragedy.

> *Friar Lawrence.* To-morrow night look that thou
>   lie alone,
> Let not the nurse lie with thee in thy chamber.
> Take thou this vial, being then in bed,
> And this distilled liquor drink thou off;
> When presently through all thy veins shall run
> A cold and drowsy humour; for no pulse
> Shall keep his native progress, but surcease;

No warmth, no breath, shall testify thou livest;
The roses in thy lips and cheeks shall fade
To paly ashes, thy eyes' windows fall,
Like death when he shuts up the day of life;
Each part, depriv'd of supple government,
Shall, stiff and stark and cold, appear like death;
And in this borrow'd likeness of shrunk death
Thou shalt continue two and forty hours,
And then awake as from a pleasant sleep.
Now, when the bridegroom in the morning comes
To rouse thee from thy bed, there art thou dead.

R. & J., IV, 1, 91-108.

Mandragors as an opiate was frequently used in Elizabethan medicine. It had, indeed, been used as such since it was prescribed by Hippocrates. It was derived from the plant *atropia mandragora*. The root is forked and the whole plant was supposed to resemble the human form. The popular superstition of the time held that when the plant was pulled out of the ground it groaned like a human being. Those who pulled up the plant and heard the groan were either killed or went mad. Shakespeare twice refers to madragora as an opiate.

Iago.   Not poppy, nor mandragora,
Nor all the drowsy syrups of the world,
Shall ever medicine thee to that sweet sleep
Which thou owed'st yesterday.

Othello, III, 3, 334-337.

Cleopatra.   Give me to drink mandragora.

Charmian.   Why, madam?

Cleopatra.   That I might sleep out this great
gap of time
My Antony is away.

A. & C., I, 5, 4-6.

Webster also knew the opiate.

Duchess.   Come, violent death,
Serve for mandragora to make me sleep!

The Duchess of Malfi, IV, 2, 237-238.

Shakespeare mentions the plant and the superstition too.

Would curses kill as doth the mandrake's groan.

> *2 H. VI*, III, 2, 310.

And shrieks like mandrakes' torn out of the earth,
That living mortals, hearing them, run mad.

> *R. & J.*, IV, 3, 48.

That whoreson mandrake, thou art fitter to be worn in my cap
than to wait at my heels.

> *2 H. IV*, I, 2, 16.

'A was the very genius of famine; yet lecherous as a monkey,
and the whores call'd him mandrake.

> *2 H. IV*, III, 2, 342.

Webster also knew the plant.

> *Flamineo.*   But as we seldom find the mistletoe
> Sacred to physic, or the builder oak,
> Without a mandrake by it; so in our quest of gain,
> Alas, the poorest of their forced dislikes
> At a limb profers, but at heart it strikes!
>
> > *The White Devil*, II, 4, 54-59.

Opiates were, however, not always regarded with favour by
Shakespeare's contemporaries.

> *Corbaccio.*   Good! he should take
> Some counsel of physicians: I have brought him
> An opiate here, from mine own doctor.
>
> *Mosca.*   He will not hear of drugs.
>
> *Corbaccio.*   Why? I myself
> Stood by while it was made, saw all the ingredients:
> And know, it cannot but mostly gently work:
> My life for his, 'tis but to make him sleep.
>
> *Volpone.*   Ay, his last sleep, if he would take it. [*Aside*].
>
> *Mosca.*   Sir, he has no faith in physic.
>
> > *Volpone*, I, 1.
>
> *Mosca.*   This is true physic, this your sacred medicine;
> No talk of opiates, to this great elixir!
>
> *Corbaccio.*   'Tis aurum palpabile, if not potabile.
>
> > *Volpone*, I, 1.

The search for and the belief in the 'elixir vitæ' was wide-spread.

> *Subtle.* This is the day I am to perfect for him
> The magisterium, our great work, the stone;
> And yield it, made, into his hands: of which
> He has, this month, talk'd as he were possess'd.
> And now he's dealing pieces on't away.—
> Methinks I see him entering ordinaries,
> Dispensing for the pox, and plaguy houses,
> Reaching his dose, walking Moorfields for lepers,
> And offering citizens' wives pomander-bracelets,
> As his preservative, made of the elixir;
> Searching the spittal, to make old bawds young;
> And the highways, for beggars, to make rich;
> I see no end of his labours. He will make
> Nature asham'd of her long sleep: when art
> Who's but a step-dame, shall do no more than she,
> In her best love to mankind, ever could:
> If his dream lasts, he'll turn the age to gold.
>
> *The Alchemist,* I, 1.

In *Volpone*, Ben Jonson exposes for us the quackery of Eliza-bethan medicine in the mountebank scene, and Nano's song summarises the whole sorry fraud.

> Had old Hippocrates, or Galen,
> That to their books put med'cines all in,
> But known this secret, they had never
> (Of which they will be guilty ever)
> Been murderers of so much paper,
> Or wasted many a hurtless taper;
> No Indian drug had e'er been famed,
> Tobacco, sassafras not named;
> Ne yet, of guacum one small stick, sir,
> Nor Raymund Lully's great elixir.
> Ne had been known the Danish Gonswart,
> Or Paracelsus, with his long sword.
>
> You that would last long, list to my song,
> Make no more coil, but buy this oil.
> Would you be ever fair and young?

Stout of teeth, and strong of tongue?
Tart of palate? quick of ear?
Sharp of sight? of nostril clear?
Moist of hand? and light of foot?
Or, I will come nearer to 't,
Would you live free from all diseases?
Do the act your mistress pleases,
Yet fright all aches from your bones?
Here's a medicine for the nones.

Volpone, II, 1.

The horrible Elizabethan medicines are mentioned by the contemporary dramatists, but, apart from the Witches' cauldron, are not given any prominence by Shakespeare.

Gasparo.   Your followers
Have swallowed you like mummia and, being sick
With such unnatural and horrid physic,
Vomit you up i' the kennel.

The White Devil, I, 1, 17-20.

Zanche.   I have blood
As red as either of theirs: wilt drink some?
'Tis good for the falling sickness. I am proud
Death cannot alter my complexion,
For I shall ne'er look pale.

The White Devil, V, 6, 228-230.

Michael. Aye, I pray, mother; in truth my feet are full of chilblains with travelling.

Wife. Faith, and those chilblains are a foul trouble. Mistress Merrythought, when your youth comes home, let him rub all the soles of his feet, and his heels, and his ankles, with a mouse-skin; or, if none of your people can catch a mouse, when he goes to bed, let him roll his feet in the warm embers, and, I warrant you, he shall be well; and you may make him put his fingers between his toes, and smell them; it's very sovereign for his head, if he be costive.

Knight of the Burning Pestle, III, 2, 58-69.

By contrast, Shakespeare records some of the less unpleasant drug habits of the Elizabethans. The pouncet-box contained extracts of sweet-smelling herbs which were thought to protect one from infectious vapours, like the plague, etc.

> *Hotspur.*   And 'twixt his finger and his thumb
> he held
> A pouncet-box, which ever and anon
> He gave his nose and took't away again;
> Who therewith angry, when it next came there,
> Took it in snuff.
>
> 1 *H. IV*, I, 3, 37-41.

Bucknill thought, wrongly, I feel, that this reference to 'snuff' was Shakespeare's only mention of tobacco. But the reference surely means the old usage of 'to snuff', i.e. to take offence at; and the nose would have good reason:

> *Hotspur.*   And as the soldiers bore dead bodies by,
> He call'd them untaught knaves, unmannerly,
> To bring a slovenly unhandsome corse
> Betwixt the wind and his nobility.
>
> 1 *H. IV*, I, 3, 42-45.

Something akin to our aperitif or cocktail was known also to Shakespeare.

> Like as to make our appetites more keen
> With eager compounds we our palate urge,
> As to prevent our maladies unseen
> We sicken to shun sickness when we purge;
> Even so, being full of your ne'er-cloying sweetness,
> To bitter sauces did I frame my feeding,
> And, sick of welfare, found a kind of meetness
> To be diseas'd ere that there was true needing.
> Thus policy in love, t' anticipate
> The ills that were not, grew to faults assured,
> And brought to medicine a healthful state,
> Which, rank of goodness, would by ill be cured.
>   But thence I learn, and find the lesson true,
>   Drugs poison him that so fell sick of you.
>
> *Sonnet,* 118.

The happy domestic picture of the weaning of an infant is recorded, and the method used—with wormwood on the nipple—though crude, would be none the less effective. I doubt, however, if our modern psychologists would approve of it.

Nurse.   And she was wean'd—I never shall forget it—
Of all the days of the year, upon that day;
For I had then laid wormwood to my dug.

. . . .

When it did taste the wormwood on the nipple
Of my dug, and felt it bitter, pretty fool,
To see it tetchy, and fall out with the dug!

R. & J., I, 3, 25-28: 31-33.

Unfortunately no details of the sea-sick cure are given.

Pisanio.   My noble mistress,
Here is a box; I had it from the Queen.
What's in't is precious. If you are sick at sea
Or stomach-qualm'd at land, a dram of this
Will drive away distemper.

Cymbeline, III, 4, 186-190.

Shakespeare does, however, occasionally name a drug.
When he mentions Carduus Benedictus, he was referring to
a very popular drug of his day, but he was also punning on
the name Benedick, Beatrice's lover.

Margaret. Get you some of this distill'd Carduus Benedictus,
and lay it to your heart; it is the only thing for a qualm.

Hero.   There thou prick'st her with a thistle.

Beatrice. Benedictus! why Benedictus? You have some moral
in this 'Benedictus'.

Margaret. Moral? No, by my troth, I have no moral meaning;
I meant plain holy-thistle.

Much Ado, III, 4, 65-72.

Carduus Benedictus, or the Holy Thistle, was considered an
almost universal panacea. Beaumont and Fletcher mention
one of its uses.

Wife. Faith, the child hath a sweet breath, George; but I
think it be troubled with the worms; carduus benedictus and
mare's milk were the only thing in the world for't.

Knight of the Burning Pestle, III, 3, 27-30.

13

Woodall in 'The Surgions Mate', 1617, lists it as one of the 'herbs most fit to be carried' at sea and claims that it

> doth ease the paine of the head, confirmeth the memory, cureth a Quartane, provoketh sweat, and comforteth the vital spirits.

In his *The Garden of Health*, 1633, William Langham lists the virtues of the drug under sixty-six heads; and as late as 1693, Salmon in *Seplasium, or Druggist Shop opened*, records fifteen preparations of the thistle then in use.

> It is excellent against pleurisie, obstructions, malign humours, vertigo, worms, agues, plague, cures green wounds, and is good against the biting of mad dogs or any other venomous creatures.

Many of the drugs mentioned by Shakespeare's contemporary dramatists are not to be found in Shakespeare, nor are the purposes for which they are used mentioned by Shakespeare.

> *Ralph.* But what brave spirit could be content to sit in his shop with a flappet of wood, and a blue apron before him, selling mithridatum and dragon's water to visited houses that, might pursue feats of arms, and, through his noble achievements, procure such a famous history to be written of his heroic prowess?
>
> *Knight of the Burning Pestle*, I, 3, 50-56.

Dragon's blood was being used as a medicine as late as 1708. 'The Learned Monsieur Tournefort, Botanist to the French King' [1] gives this information about it:

> The Dragon-Tree of Clusius growing plentifully upon the Canary Islands; and appearing to be a kind of Date tree.
>
> The Trunk of this tree is very rough, and full of clefts and chaps pouring forth a Liquor during the heat of the Dog-Days, which afterwards thickens or concretes into red-colour'd Drops or Tears, call'd Dragons-blood: The which Dragons-Blood, tho it is hardly dissolv'd in watry or oily Liquors; yet it ought to be reckon'd among the Gums and Robins.
>
> Dragons-Blood is of a dark red Colour, easily takes fire, and dies a Paper or hot Glass with a noble Crimson Colour.

[1] Tournefort. *Materia Medica.* 1708.

Virtues. Dragons-Blood and Catechu are useful in restraining or stopping all sorts of Fluxes; but especially spitting of Blood, Hemorrhages, and others of that Nature.

As a means of inducing patients to swallow some unpalatable medicine butter was used in the form of a pill, the method being attributed to the Dutch.

> *Mosca.* You shall have some will swallow
> A melting heir as glibly as your Dutch
> Will pills of butter, and ne'er purge for it.
>
> *Volpone*, I, 1.

> *Ralph.* Now butter with a leaf of sage is good to purge the
> blood;
> Fly Venus and phlebotomy, for they are neither good.
>
> *Knight of the Burning Pestle*, IV, 5, 99-100.

Advice on slimming is offered by Beaumont and Fletcher.

> *Galatea.* Full being! I understand you not, unless your grace means growing to fatness; and then your only remedy (upon my knowledge, prince) is, in a morning, a cup of neat white wine brewed with carduus, then fast till supper; about eight you may eat; use exercise, and keep a sparrow-hawk; you can shoot in a tiller: but, of all, your grace must fly phlebotomy, fresh pork, conger, and clarified whey; they are dullers of the vital spirits.
>
> *Philaster*, II, 2, 37-46.

The Host in *The Merry Wives* believed in potions, as did the Physician in Tamburlaine.

> *Host.* Shall I lose my doctor? no; he gives me the potions and the motions.
>
> *The Merry Wives of Windsor*, III, 1, 9.

> *1st Physician.* Pleaseth your majesty to drink
> this potion,
> Which will abate the fury of your fit
> And cause some milder spirits govern you.
>
> *Tamburlaine the Great*, V, 3.

Webster, however, had no faith in love-potions.

> *Ferdinand.* Can your faith give way
> To think there's power in potions or in charms,
> To make us love whether we will or no?

> *Bosola.* Most certainly.
>
> *Ferdinand.* Away! these are mere gulleries,
> horrid things,
> Invented by some cheating mountebanks
> To abuse us. Do you think that herbs or charms
> Can force the will? Some trials have been made
> In this foolish practice, but the ingredients
> Were lenitive poisons, such as are of force
> To make the patient mad; and straight the witch
> Swears by equivocation they are in love.
>
> *The Duchess of Malfi*, III, 1, 67-77.

The efficacy of aphrodisiacs, or 'provocative electuaries' as Webster called them, were as much in question as love-potions.

> *Flamineo.* Women are more willing and more gloriously chaste when they are least restrained of their liberty. It seems you would be a fine capricious mathematically jealous coxcomb; take the height of your own horns with a Jacob's staff afore they are up. These politic enclosures for paltry mutton make more rebellion in the flesh than all the provocative electuaries doctors have uttered since last jubilee.
>
> *The White Devil*, I, 2, 94-102.

> *Cleremont.* Sure this lady has a good turn done her against her will; before she was common talk, now none dare say cantharides can stir her.
>
> *Philaster*, IV, 1, 44-46.

It is rare to find Shakespeare naming poisons, e.g. ratsbane, or hebenon (or hebona). But his clinical description of the action of a poison is so terse and realistic that it could almost be a description by a witness at first hand. Even now it might be with advantage included in a modern text-book of Toxicology.

> *Prince Henry.* How fares your Majesty?
>
> *King John.* Poison'd—ill-fare! Dead, forsook, cast off;
> And none of you will bid the winter come
> To thrust his icy fingers in my maw,

Nor let my Kingdom's rivers take their course
Through my burn'd bosom, nor entreat the north
To make his bleak winds kiss my parched lips
And comfort me with cold. I do not ask you much;
I beg cold comfort; and you are strait
And so ingrateful you deny me that.
   Prince Henry. O that there were some virtue in my
                      tears,
That might relieve you!
   King John.   The salt in them is hot.
Within me is a hell; and there the poison
Is as a fiend confin'd to tyrannise
On unreprievable condemned blood.
King John, V, 7, 34-48.

The Italian influence of the period is noted both in Juliet's suspicion of the good friar's sleeping-draught and Romeo's reference to 'Mantua's law'. The suspicion of poison was prevalent in the minds of the population of the time—and with just cause!—for it was the popular means, at least in the imagination of the people and certainly in the plays of the contemporary dramatists, of disposing of one's problems or enemies, or both. The Italian influence on the Elizabethans has been widely noted and especially by the late Professor Ernesto Grillo. [1]

   Juliet. What if it be a poison, which the friar
Subtly hath minister'd to have me dead,
Lest in this marriage he should be dishonour'd,
Because he married me before to Romeo?
I fear it is: and yet, methinks, it should not,
For he hath still been tried a holy man.
Romeo and Juliet, IV, 3, 24-29.

   Romeo. Come hither, man. I see that thou art
         poor;
Hold, there is forty ducats: let me have
A dram of poison; such soon-speeding gear
As will disperse itself through the veins,

[1] Grillo, Professor Ernesto, *Shakespeare and Italy*. Robert Maclehose & Co., Ltd., The University Press, Glasgow. (Privately printed, 1949).

> That the life-weary taker may fall dead,
> And that the trunk may be discharged of breath
> As violently as hasty powder fired
> Doth hurry from the fatal cannon's womb.
>
>   *Apothecary.*   Such mortal drugs I have; but Mantua's
>   law
> Is death to any he that utters them.
>
> *Romeo and Juliet*, V, 1, 58-67.

Marlowe says quite clearly where his knowledge of poisoning originates:

> *Lightborn.*   You shall not need to give instructions;
> 'Tis not the first time I have kill'd a man:
> I learned in Naples how to poison flowers;
> To strangle with a lawn thrust down the throat;
> To pierce the wind pipe with a needle's point;
> Or, whilst one is asleep, to take a quill,
> And blow a little powder in his ears;
> Or open his mouth, and pour quick-silver down.
>
> *Edward the Second.*

Shakespeare, as already noted, used the ears as a route for the poison—the juice of cursed hebenon. The possible source of his information is discussed in the chapter on 'The Medical Problems of the Tragedies—How did Hamlet's Father die?' (q.v.). But Shakespeare gives no clue to the nature of the poisonous ointment used by Laertes to anoint his sword.

> *Laertes.*   I will do't;
> And for that purpose I'll anoint my sword.
> I bought an unction of a mountebank,
> So mortal that but dip a knife in it,
> Where it draws blood no cataplasm so rare,
> Collected from all simples that have virtue
> Under the moon, can save the thing from death
> That is but scratch'd withal: I'll touch my point
> With this contagion, that, if I gall him slightly,
> It may be death.
>
> *Hamlet*, IV, 7, 139-148.

Cleopatra's attitude is in the grand manner and is founded on her own knowledge: she had 'pursued conclusions infinite of easy ways to die.'

> *Cleopatra.* Have I the aspic in my lips? Dost
> fall?
> If thou and nature can so gently part,
> The stroke of death is as a lover's pinch,
> Which hurts, and is desired. Dost thou lie still?
> If thus thou vanishest, thou tell'st the world
> It is not worth leave-taking.
>
> *Antony and Cleopatra*, V, 2, 291-296.

Of this grand manner, Professor Grillo [1] comments

> From the Italian Epicureans of the Renaissance English play-
> wrights learned that 'joie de vivre' and stoicism in facing death
> which are so impressively portrayed by Shakespeare, Marlowe,
> Beaumont and Fletcher, and even by the 'wild and savage
> Webster'.

Shakespeare's main source for the story of Antony and Cleopatra was Plutarch's life of Antony, and Plutarch [2] leaves us in no doubt about what Cleopatra had in mind when, in Shakespeare's euphemism, she 'pursued conclusions infinite of easy ways to die'.

> 'But Cleopatra', Plutarch writes, 'was busied in making a col-
> lection of all varieties of poisonous drugs, and, in order to see
> which of them were the least painful in the operation, she had
> them tried upon prisoners condemned to die. But, finding that
> the quick poisons always worked with sharp pains, and that the
> less painful were slow, she next tried venomous animals, and
> watching with her own eyes whilst they were applied, one
> creature to the body of another. This was her daily practice,
> and she pretty well satisfied herself that nothing was comparable
> to the bite of an asp, which, without convulsion or groaning,
> brought on a heavy drowsiness and lethargy, with a gentle
> sweat on the face, the senses being stupefied by degrees; the

---

[1] Grillo, Professor Ernesto, *Shakespeare and Italy*. Robert Maclehose & Co., Ltd., The University Press, Glasgow. (Privately printed, 1949).
[2] Plutarch's Lives, III, 318-319. (Everyman's Library).

patient in appearance, being sensible of no pain, but rather troubled to be disturbed or awakened like those that are in a profound sleep.'

The spider was also considered poisonous and could be given in a drink. No less an authority than Ambroise Paré wrote:

> The ancients have thought the bitings of spiders to be venomous. Now their poison is, therefore, thought to be cold, because the symptoms thence arising are winde in the belly, refrigerations of the extreme parts of the body, numbesse in the bitten part, with sense of cold and shaking.

Shakespeare knew of this belief.

> *Leontes.*   There may be in the cup
> A spider steep'd, and one may drink, depart,
> And yet partake no venom, for his knowledge
> Is not infected; but if one present
> Th' abhorr'd ingredient to his eye, make known
> How he hath drunk, he cracks his gorge, his sides,
> With violent hefts. I have drunk, and seen the spider.
> > *The Winter's Tale*, II, 1, 39-45.

Webster also refers to it.

> *Isabella.*   I do beseech you,
> Entreat him mildly; let not your rough tongue
> Set us at louder variance; all my wrongs
> Are freely pardoned; and I do not doubt,
> As men, to try the precious unicorn's horn,
> Make of the powder a preservative circle,
> And in it put a spider, so these arms
> Shall charm his poison, force it to obeying,
> And keep him chaste from an infected straying.
> > *The White Devil*, II, 1, 10-18.

The Italian influence, and in particular the methods of poisoning which, rightly or wrongly, we have come to associate with the Borgias, is clear in Webster's references to poisons. The three instances from the *The White Devil* will suffice to illustrate the point.

Flamineo. My lord, do you mark their whispering? I will compound a medicine, out of their two heads, stronger than garlic, deadlier than stibium: the cantharides, which are scarce seen to stick upon the flesh when they work to the heart, shall not do it with more silence or invisible cunning.

The White Devil, II, 1, 280-285.

Conjuror.   She's poisoned
By the fumed picture. 'Twas her custom nightly
Before she went to bed, to go and visit
Your picture, and to feed her eyes and lips
On the dead shadow. Doctor Julio,
Observing this, infects it with an oil
And other poisoned stuff, which presently
Did suffocate her spirits.

The White Devil, II, 3, 23-31.

Lodovico. T' have poisoned his prayer-book, or a
          pair of beads,
The pummel of his saddle, his looking-glass,
Or th' handle of his racket. Oh, that, that!
That while he had been bandying at tennis,
He might have sworn himself to hell, and strook
His soul into the hazard.

The White Devil, V, 1, 71-76

Chapter Eleven

SHAKESPEARE ON WOUNDS

A broadsword or dagger was the invariable equipment of every ordinary man qualified to wear weapons. At the beginning of Elizabeth's reign even agricultural labourers, when at work, put down in a corner of the field their sword, buckler, and bow. London apprentices, however, were forbidden to carry any weapon but a knife.

Shakespeare's England, Vol. II, Ch. XIX, p. 112.
Costume—P. Macquoid. (1950).

The examples of the contemporary duel (in *As You Like It* and *Twelfth Night*) have already been referred to, and in these it appears that Shakespeare deliberately set out to ridicule current practice. Whether it was owing to the direct encouragement of the Queen, or to the introduction of the easily manipulated and universally worn rapier as the favourite weapon of a gentleman, it is a fact that duelling in these days almost bore the aspect of a social contagious disease.

James I, however, regarded duelling as 'a vaine that bleeds both incessantly and inwardly', and resolutely discountenanced the practice; his 'Proclamation against private Challenges and Combats' appeared in 1613 (in conformity with which Lord Sanquhar was executed for the 'murder' of his fencing-master), and in 1615, when Bacon was attorney-general, the Star Chamber 'with one consent did utterly reject and condemne the opinion that the private duel in any person whatsoever had any ground of honor.'

Shakespeare's England, Vol. II, Ch. XXVII, pp. 405-406.
Fencing and Duelling—A. Florbes Sieveking.

IN the robust vigour of Elizabethan life, wounds were a common medical experience. It is difficult for us to realise in that pre-antibiotic, pre-antiseptic period of surgery what the treatment of wounds was like. Only the vaguest ideas of healing existed and even these were the result of lay, and not necessarily medical, observation. Shakespeare's acutely observant eye has recorded many of the views about wounds which must have been very much the everyday concern of the Elizabethans. Something of their ideas on the treatment of wounds can be inferred from Shakespeare's use of the wound-image in his metaphors.

Corrosives were applied to serious and dangerous wounds.

> *Queen.* Away! Though parting be a fretful corrosive,
> It is applied to a deathful wound
>
> *2 Henry VI*, III, 2, 403-404.

Massinger expresses the same view.

> *Wellborn.* Wounds of this nature are not to be cured
> With balms, but corrosives.
>
> *A New Way to Pay Old Debts*, I, 1, 134-135.

The 'balms' were also mentioned by Shakespeare.

> *Alcibiades.* Is this the balsam that the usurping Senate
> Pours into captains' wounds?
>
> *Timon of Athens*, III, 5, 110-111.

> 'Tis not enough that through the cloud thou break
> To dry the rain on my storm-beaten face,
> For no man well of such a salve can speak
> That heals the wound, and cures not the disgrace.
>
> *Sonnet*, XXXIV.

Plasters were used for some types of wound.

> *Gonzalo.* You rub the sore,
> When you should bring the plaster.
>
> *The Tempest*, II, 2, 132-133.

> *Salisbury.* I am not glad that such a sore of time
> Should seek a plaster by contemn'd revolt,
> And heal the inveterate canker of one wound
> By making many.
>
> *King John*, V, 2, 12-15.

> Here kennell'd in a brake she finds a hound,
> And asks the weary caitiff for his master;
> And there another licking of his wound,

> 'Gainst venom'd sores the only sovereign plaster;
> And here she meets another sadly scowling,
> To whom she speaks, and he replies with howling.
>
> *Venus and Adonis*, 913-918.

Webster also refers to this form of treatment.

> *Flamineo.*   For I have known men that have come from serving
> against the Turk, for three or four months they have had pension
> to buy them new wooden legs and fresh plasters; but, after,
> 'twas not to be had.
>
> *The White Devil*, V, 1.

An explanation of the use of a 'tent' in the treatment of
wounds is necessary to make the following references clear.
A 'tent' was a roll of lint or flax, which was thrust into a deep
wound to control bleeding, in the first place, and also to
absorb the subsequent discharge from the wound. Naturally
when the test had absorbed blood or discharge, it swelled
and caused pain when it had to be removed. It served the
purpose, too, of not allowing the wound to heal too quickly.
Wounds in these days were expected to suppurate. If the
discharge was free and 'sweet', it was called 'laudable pus'.
The wounds healed by granulation tissue, or 'proud flesh',
which grew from the depth outwards until it formed a solid,
deep scar.

Shakespeare uses 'tent', of course, in its ordinary, accepted
sense:

> *Cominius.*   Go we to our tent,
> The blood upon your visage dries; 'tis time
> It should be look'd to. Come.
>
> *Coriolanus*, I, 9, 92-94.

but earlier in this same scene he uses it in its surgical sense, and
also on five other occasions. Unless we know of the surgical
reference, Thersites' reply is meaningless.

> *Patroclus.*   Who keeps the tent now?
> *Thersites.*   The surgeon's box or the patient's
>   wound.
>
> *Troilus and Cressida*, V, 1, 10-11.

Hector and Imogen both use it in its correct surgical meaning.

> *Hector.* The wound of peace is surety,
> Surety secure; but modest doubt is call'd
> The beacon of the wise, the tent that searches
> To th' bottom of the worst.
> > *Troilus and Cressida,* II, 2, 14-17.

> *Imogen.* Talk thy tongue weary—speak.
> I have heard I am a strumpet, and mine ear,
> Therein false struck, can take no greater wound,
> Nor tent to bottom that.
> > *Cymbeline,* III, 4, 111-114.

Lear and Cominius comment on the danger of omitting the use of a tent.

> *Lear.* Blasts and fogs upon thee!
> Th' untented woundings of a father's curse
> Pierce every sense about thee!
> > *Lear,* I, 4, 299-301.

> *Caius Marcius.* I have some wounds upon me,
> > and they smart
> To hear themselves rememb'red.
> *Cominius.* Should they not,
> Well might they fester 'gainst ingratitude
> And tent themselves with death.
> > *Coriolanus,* I, 9, 27-31.

> *Menenius.* For 'tis a sore upon us
> You cannot tent yourself!
> > *Coriolanus,* III, 1, 235-236.

Webster was also familiar with the surgical use of the tent.

> *Ferdinand.* Why, to make soft lint for his mother's
> > wounds,
> When I have hewed her to pieces.
> > *The Duchess of Malfi,* II, 5, 30-31.

Ferdinand. And of a jest she broke of a captain she met full of wounds: I have forgot it.

Castruchio. She told him, my lord, he was a pitiful fellow, to lie, like the children of Ismael, all in tents.

Ferdinand. Why, there's a wit were able to undo all the chirurgeons o' the city.
> *The Duchess of Malfi,* I, 1, 118-124.

> *Flamineo.* I ever thought a cutler should distinguish
> The cause of my death, rather than a doctor.
> Search my wound deeper; tent it with the steel
> That made it.
>
> *The White Devil*, V, 6, 236-239.

Shakespeare knew that during the excitement of battle—
and in his day that meant close personal combat—wounds
could remain painless; but when the mental tension of the
action was over, pain would become apparent. Hotspur's
experience of this partly explains his anger when he was so
'pest'red with a popinjay'; but it appears he was also stung
by the reference to an 'inward bruise' when he was experi-
encing the 'grief' of gaping wounds.

> *Hotspur.* My liege, I did deny no prisoners.
> But I remember when the fight was done,
> When I was dry with rage and extreme toil,
> Breathless and faint, leaning upon my sword,
> Came there a certain lord, neat, and trimly dress'd,
> Fresh as a bridegroom, and his chin new reap'd
> Show'd like a stubble-land at harvest-home.
> He was perfumed like a milliner,
> And 'twixt his finger and his thumb he held
> A pouncet-box, which ever and anon
> He gave his nose and took 't away again;
> Who therewith angry, when it next came there,
> Took it in snuff—and still he smil'd and talk'd—
> And as the soldiers bore dead bodies by,
> He call'd them untaught knaves, unmannerly,
> To bring a slovenly unhandsome corse
> Betwixt the wind and his nobility.
> With many holiday and lady terms
> He questioned me: amongst the rest, demanded
> My prisoners in your Majesty's behalf.
> I then, all smarting with my wounds being cold,
> To be so pest'red with a popinjay,
> Out of my grief and my impatience
> Answer'd neglectingly I know not what—
> He should, or he should not—for he made me mad

To see him shine so brisk, and smell so sweet,
And talk so like a waiting-gentlewoman
Of guns, and drums, and wounds—God sake the mark!—
And telling me the sovereignest thing on earth
Was parmaceti for an inward bruise.

1 Henry IV, I, 3, 29-58.

Parmaceti has already been mentioned in the chapter on Elizabethan Medicine, as has also the use of the plantain leaf.

> *Romeo.* Your plantain leaf is excellent for that.
>
> *Benvolio.* For what, I pray thee?
>
> *Romeo.* For your broken shin.

R. & J., I, 2, 50-51.

Hotspur's anger could be compared to that of the lion in Marlowe's reference to wounds in *Edward II.*

> The forest deer, being struck,
> Runs to an herb that closeth up the wounds.
> But when the imperial lion's flesh is gor'd,
> He rends and tears it with his wrathful paw,
> (And), highly scorning that the lowly earth
> Should drink his blood, mounts up to the air.

The Elizabethan belief in the miraculous healing of a wound, as in the case of the deer, extended also to the King who could heal the King's Evil.

> *Malcolm.* Comes the King forth, I pray you?
>
> *Doctor.* Ay, sir. There are a crew of wretched souls
> That stay his cure. Their malady convinces
> The great assay of art; but at his touch,
> Such sanctity hath heaven given his hand,
> They presently amend.
>
> *Malcolm.* I thank you, doctor.   [*Exit Doctor.*
>
> *Macduff.* What's the disease he means?
>
> *Malcolm.*   'Tis called the evil:
> A most miraculous work in this good king;
> Which often since my here-remain in England
> I have seen him do. How he solicits heaven,

> Himself best knows; but strangely-visited people,
> All swoln and ulcerous, pitiful to the eye,
> The mere despair of surgery, he cures,
> Hanging a golden stamp about their necks,
> Put on with holy prayers; and 'tis spoken,
> To the succeeding royalty he leaves
> The healing benediction. With this strange virtue,
> He hath a heavenly gift of prophecy;
> And sundry blessings hang about his throne
> That speak him full of grace.
>
> *Macbeth*, IV, 3, 140-159.

'Green wounds' were a hopeful sign of healing, possibly because the colour was due to 'laudable pus'.

> *Post.* Send succours, lords, and stop the rage betime,
> Before the wound do grow uncurable;
> For, being green, there is great hope of help.
>
> 2 *Henry VI*, 1, 285-287.

> *Quickly.* Did not goodwife Keech, the butcher's wife, come in then and call me gossip Quickly? Coming in to borrow a mess of vinegar, telling us she had a good dish of prawns, whereby thou didst desire to eat some, whereby I told thee they were ill for a green wound?
>
> 2 *Henry IV*, II, 1, 90-94.

Hæmorrhage from wounds was, of course, a very serious matter in Shakespeare's day, when there were few effective means of controlling it. Ligatures and the cautery were used and pressure could be applied by the insertion of a 'tent'.

> *Portia.* Have by some surgeon, Shylock, on your
> charge,
> To stop his wounds, lest he do bleed to death.
>
> *Merchant of Venice*, IV, 1, 252-253.

> *Clifford.* The air hath got into my deadly wounds,
> And much effuse of blood doth make me faint.
>
> 3 *Henry VI*, II, 6, 27-28.

Marlowe's description of a bullet wound includes also the Elizabethan conception of the circulation before Harvey's discovery.

> *Captain.* A deadly bullet gliding through my side,
> Lies heavy on my heart; I cannot live:
> I feel my liver pierc'd, and all my veins,
> That there begin and nourish every part
> Mangled and torn, and all my entrails bath'd
> In blood that straineth from their orifex.
>
> > 2 *Tamburlaine the Great*, III, 4.

Juliet's garrulous Nurse obviously relished the gory details.

> *Nurse.* I saw the wound, I saw it with mine eyes—
> God save the mark!—here on his manly breast.
> A piteous corse, a bloody piteous corse;
> Pale, pale as ashes, all bedaub'd in blood,
> All in gore-blood. I swounded at the sight.
>
> > *R. & J.*, III, 2, 52-56.

Two methods of household medicine in controlling bleeding
are mentioned.

> *Bottom.* I shall desire you of more acquaintance, good Master
> Cobweb. If I cut my finger, I shall make bold with you.
>
> > *Midsummer Night's Dream*, III, 1, 168-170.

> *Servant.* I'll fetch some flax and whites of eggs
> To apply to his bleeding face.
>
> > *Lear*, III, 7, 105-106.

From Webster we learn that some wounds were stitched.

> *Flamineo.* Look, his eye's bloodshed, like a needle a chirurgeon
> stitched a wound with.
>
> > *The White Devil*, II, 1, 308-309.

Shakespeare must have seen many types of wounds for he
describes a variety of them.

> *Exeter.*   And York, all haggled over,
> Comes to him, where in gore he lay insteeped,
> And takes him by the beard, kisses the gashes
> That bloodily did yawn upon his face.
>
> > *Henry V*, IV, 6, 11-14.

> *Antony.* Over thy wounds now do I prophesy—
> Which like dumb mouths do ope their ruby lips
> To beg the voice and utterance of my tongue.
>
> > *Julius Cæsar*, III, 1, 260-262.

Hamlet. It will but skin and film the ulcerous place,
Whiles rank corruption, mining all within,
Infects unseen.

Hamlet, III, 4, 147-149.

(Sir Philip Sidney [1554-86])—*Apology for Poetry*—written only ten years before Shakespeare began to work in the London theatre—Tragedy—'openeth the greatest wounds, and showeth forth the ulcers that are covered with Tissue.')

Duncan. So well thy words become thee as thy
                    wounds;
They smack of honour both.—Go get him surgeons.

Macbeth, I, 2, 44-45.

Antony. Thou bleed'st apace.

Scarus. I had a wound here that was like a T,
But now 'tis made an H.

Antony and Cleopatra, IV, 7, 6-8.

Sicinius. He's a disease that must be cut away.

Meninius. O, he's a limb that has but a disease—
Mortal to cut it off: to cure it easy.

. . . .

Sicinius.   The service of the foot,
Being once gangren'd, is not then respected
For what before it was.

Coriolanus, III, 1, 295-297: 306-308.

Achilles. I see my reputation is at stake;
My fame is shrewdly gor'd.

Patroclus.   O, then, beware:
Those wounds heal ill that men do give themselves.

Troilus and Cressida, III, 3, 227-230.

Wounds healed slowly in those days and even the merest scratch left its scar.

Iago. How poor are they that have not
                patience!
What wound did ever heal but by degrees?

Othello, II, 3, 358-359.

Justice. I am loath to gall a new-heal'd wound.

2 *Henry IV*, I, 2, 139.

Phebe.   Now show the wound mine eye hath
                        made in thee.
Scratch thee but with a pin, and there remains
Some scar of it; lean upon a rush,
The cicatrice and capable impressure
Thy palm some moment keeps; but now mine eyes,
Which I have darted at thee, hurt thee not;
Nor, I am sure, there is not force in eyes
That can do hurt.

> *As You Like It*, III, 5, 20-27.

Though, happily, almost unknown here now, the 'bite of a mad dog' (rabies) was as much feared in Elizabethan days as it is in the East to-day.

Margaret.   O Buckingham, take heed of yonder
                        dog!
Look when he fawns, he bites; and when he bites,
His venom tooth will rankle to the death.

> *Richard III*, I, 3, 289-291.

Abbess.   And thereof came it that the man was
                        mad.
The venom clamours of a jealous woman
Poisons more deadly than a mad dog's tooth.

> *Comedy of Errors*, V, 1, 68-70.

Falstaff's feelings before the battle of Shrewsbury can be the more appreciated when we read, in some of Shakespeare's fellow-dramatists, of the plight of the ex-servicemen of those days.

Falstaff. I would 'twere bed-time, Hal, and all well.
Prince. Why, thou owest God a death.   [*Exit.*
Falstaff. 'Tis not due yet; I would be loath to pay him before his day. What need I be so forward with him that calls not on me? Well, 'tis no matter; honour pricks me on. Yea, but how if honour prick me off when I come on? How then? Can honour set to a leg? No. Or an arm? No. Or take away the grief of a wound? No. Honour hath no skill in surgery, then? No. What is honour? A word. What is in that word? Honour. What is that honour? Air. A trim reckoning! Who hath it? He that died o' Wednesday. Doth he feel it? No. Doth he hear it? No.

'Tis insensible, then? Yea, to the dead. But will it not live with the living? No. Why? Detraction will not suffer it. Therefore I'll none of it. Honour is a mere scutcheon. And so ends my catechism.

1 *Henry IV*, V, 1, 125-140.

Flamineo. I will now give you some politic instructions. The duke says he will give you a pension: that's but bare promise; get it under his hand. For I have known men that have come from serving against the Turk, for three or four months they have had a pension to buy them new wooden legs and fresh plasters; but, after, 'twas not to be had. And this miserable courtesy shows as if a tormentor should give hot cordial drinks to one three-quarters dead o' the rack, only to fetch the miserable soul again to endure more dog-days.

The White Devil, V, 1, 140-150.

Bosola. There are rewards for hawks and dogs when they have done us service; but for a soldier that hazards his limbs in a battle, nothing but a kind of geometry is his last supportation.

Delio. Geometry?

Bosola. Aye, to hang in a fair pair of slings, take his latter swing in the world upon an honourable pair of crutches, from hospital to hospital. Fare ye well, sir: and yet do not you scorn us; for places in the court are but like beds in the hospital, where this man's head lies at that man's foot, and so lower and lower.

The Duchess of Malfi, I, 1, 63-74.

Gaveston. Why, there are hospitals for such as you;
I have no war; and therefore, sir, be gone.

3rd Poor Man. Farewell, and perish by a soldier's hand,
That wouldst reward them with an hospital.

Edward II.

Chapter Twelve

SHAKESPEARE ON PUBLIC HEALTH AND EPIDEMICS

'The first mention found in Stratford records of John Shake-speare, the poet's father, is dated 1552, when he was fined along with two important townsmen, Adrian Quiney and Humfrey Reynolds, for making a new and unauthorised refuse-heap in Henley Street.'

'This does not prove the indifference of the magistrates to sanitation, as some have argued, but the reverse. The Corporation sold the public refuse-heaps from time to time, so that their financial interests were also threatened'.

PETER ALEXANDER,
Shakespeare's Life and Art, pp. 17-18 and footnote.

THE Plague overshadowed the whole of Shakespeare's life in the theatre. It is natural, then, to find that most of his references to the Public Health and to epidemics are coloured by the knowledge of this continual, terrifying experience. Before we can appreciate Shakespeare's references, however, we must know something of the current medical thought about the causes of the Plague, the treatment of cases, and the prevention of the spread of the infection. For this purpose a treatise on the subject, 'A defensative against the plague', written by Simon Kellwaye and published in 1593 is most enlightening. In [1] it we are told what the plague is:

all do agree that it is a pernitious and contagious feaver, and reckned to be one of the number of those which are called EPIDEMIA, chiefly proceeding of adusted and melancholike bloud, which may be easily perceived by the extreame heate and inflammation which inwardly they doe feele that are infected therewith.

[1 *Present Remedies against the Plague, etc.* Shakespeare Association Fac-similes No. 7, with an introduction by W. P. Barrett, 1933.

Eight possible sources of the infection are recorded:

over great and unnaturall heate and drieth, by great rayne and
inundatyons of waters, or by great store of rotten and stincking
bodies, both of men and beasts, lying uppon the face of the earth
unburied, as in the time of warres hath bene seene, which doth
so corrupt the ayre, as that thereby our Corne, Fruites, Herbes,
and waters which we dayly use for our foode and sustenaunce,
are infected: also it may come by some stincking doonghils,
filthie and standing pooles of water, and unsavery smelles which
are neere the places where we dwell, or by thrusting a great
compnaie of people into a close narrow, or straight roome, as
most commonly we see in shippes, common Gayles, and in
narrow and close lanes and streetes, where many people doe
dwell together, and the places not orderly kept cleane and
sweete. But most commonly in this our time it is dispersed
amongst us, by accompanying our selves with such as either have,
or lately have had the disease them selves; or at least have been
conversant with such as have bene infected therewith. But for
the most parte it doth come by receaving into our custody some
clothes, or such like things that have been used about some
infected body, wherein the infection may be hidden a long
time: as hath bene too often experimented with repentance
too late in many places. It may also come by dogs, cats, pigs,
and weasells which are prone and apt to receive and carrie the
infection from place to place. But howsoever it doth come, let
us assure our selves that it is a just punishment of God layde
upon us, for our manyfold sinnes and transgressions against his
divine Maiestie.

With that last sentence, a London preacher [1] heartily agreed
when he expressed a view that was considered unanswerable
by those who loathed the theatres:

The cause of the plague is sin, if you look at it well; and the
cause of sin are the plays; therefore the cause of plagues are plays.

The treatment of the victims is set out in a pamphlet, the
title page of which reads:

Present Remedies
against the plague.

[1] Chute, Marchette, *Shakespeare of London*, pp. 91-92.

shewing sundrye preservatives
for the same, by wholsome Fumes, drinkes, vomits
and other inward Receits; as also the perfect
cure (by Implaisture) of any that are
                    therewith infected.

Now necessary to be observed of every Housholder, to
        avoide the infection, lately begun in some
                    places of this Cittie.

Written by a learned Physition, for the health of
                    his Countrey.

Printed for Thomas Pauyer, and are to be sold at his shop
        at the entrance into the Exchange.
                    1603.

The motto of Thomas Pauyer the printer could not possibly
have appeared with a modern trade union's consent. It reads:
        Thou shalt labor till thou returne to duste.

Pauyer had an eye to quick and extensive sales and a good line
in salesmanship. He addresses himself 'To the Reader':

> For as much as the force and infection of the ordinary diseas
> called the Plague or Pestilence, hath heretofore beene too well
> knowne and felt in sundrie places of this Realme: and considering
> that it hath of late begun to increase in many chief Citties and
> populous places; I thought it good to publish to you in time,
> sundry preservatives against the said disease, the better to defende
> those that are in health, from the infection of the diseased: And
> also to cure those that are any infected, grieved, or troubled
> with the same. And to this I was imboldened, the rather for that
> it was written by a very learned and approved Phisition of our
> time, who desireth more the health of his country, than by
> discovering his name seeme vaineglorious to the world. Accept
> the same I pray you in good part, and thanke God for the
> Phisitions paines, who hath his desire if it may doe but that
> which he wisheth: namely expel sicknes, and increase health
> to this Land. Which God for his mercie sake, prosper and
> preserve from all plagues and dangers for evermore. Amen.

When these remedies have been studied, one can only re-echo
the prayer of that last sentence, that 'God for his mercie sake,

prosper and preserve this land from all plagues and dangers for evermore.   Amen.'

But the measures to prevent the spread of the infection were quite a different story.   They compare favourably with the advice given nowadays for the terrifying epidemics of Poliomyelitis.   In 1592 they were issued as:

> Orders to be used in the tyme of the Infeccon of the Plague within the Cittie and Liberties of London, till further Charitable provision be had for the Places of receipte for the Visited with infeccon.

Separate orders were issued for the rest of the country:

> Orders, thought meete, by her Maiestie, and her privie Counsell, to be executed throughout the Counties of this Realm, in such Townes, Villages, and other places, as are, or may be hereafter infected with the plague, for the stay of further increase of the same.

> Also, an advice set downe upon her Maiesties expresse commaundment, by the best learned in Physicke within this Realme, containing sundry good rules and easie medicines, without charge to the meaner sort of people, as well for the preservation of her good Subjectes from the plague before the infection, as for the curing and ordering of them after they shall be infected.

Of these orders one in particular should be recorded, for it was noted and used by Shakespeare at a crucial point in Romeo and Juliet, the point at which the tragedy becomes inevitable.

> That in every howse infected, the Master Mistris or governour, and the whole famulie and residentes therein at the tyme of such infeccon, shall remayne continuallie withowt departinge owt of the same, and with the doores and windowes, of the hall, shopp, or other nether parte of the howse shutt, by the space of xxviii dayes from the death of the partie dying of Infeccon, and untill the partie sicke and not dying thereof shalbe fullie recovered, or there sore fully healed, and suche person recoveringe or healed to tarry shutt upp xx daies from suche recovery or full healing. And that during all that tyme noe Clothes, Linnen, or other like thing be hanged owt or over into the streete.

In the play, the letter to Romeo, because of this regulation, was not delivered.

> *Friar Lawrence.* This same should be the voice
> of Friar John.
> Welcome from Mantua! What says Romeo?
> Or, if his mind be writ, give me his letter.
>
> *Friar John* Going to find a barefoot brother out,
> One of our order, to associate me,
> Here in this city visiting the sick,
> And finding him, the searchers of the town,
> Suspecting that we both were in a house
> Where the infectious pestilence did reign,
> Seal'd up the doors, and would not let us forth,
> So that my speed to Mantua there was stay'd.
>
> *Friar Lawrence.* Who bare my letter, then, to
> Romeo?
>
> *Friar John.* I could not send it—here it is again—
> Nor get a messenger to bring it thee,
> So fearful were they of infection.
>
> *R. & J.*, V, 2, 1-16.

Shakespeare was as interested as the rest of the population in all aspects of the Plague. Whether the ideas about the spread of plague expressed in the plays are his own or merely reflect the popular beliefs of his day, they are of medical interest and are worth noting. The plague, for example, could be caught from the air,

> O, when mine eyes did see Olivia first,
> Methought she purg'd the air of pestilence!
>
> *T. N.*, I, 1, 19-20.

> The blessed gods
> Purge all infection from our air whilst you
> Do climate here!
>
> *W. T.*, V, 1, 168-170.

> And for mine own part I durst not laugh, for
> fear of opening my lips and receiving the bad air.
>
> *J. C.*, I, 2, 248-249.

> What, is Brutus sick,
> And will he steal out of his wholesome bed,
> To dare the vile contagion of the night,
> And tempt the rheumy and unpurged air
> To add unto his sickness?
>
> *J. C.*, II, 1, 172-179.

> Boils and plagues
> Plaster you o'er, that you may be abhorr'd
> Farther than seen, and one infect another
> Against the wind a mile!
>
> *Cor.*, I, 4, 31-34.

> O blessed breeding sun, draw from the earth
> Rotten humidity; below thy sister's orb
> Infect the air!
>
> *Timon*, IV, 3, 1-3.

> With rotten damps ravish the morning air;
> Let their exhaled unwholesome breaths make sick
> The life of purity, the supreme fair—
>
> *The Rape of Lucrece*, 778-780.

Another means of spreading the infection directly was by the breath:

> She speaks poniards, and every word stabs; if her breath were as terrible as her terminations, there were no living near her; she would infect to the north star.
>
> *Much Ado*, II, 1, 223-225.

> But even this night, whose black contagious breath
> Already smokes about the burning crest
> Of the old, feeble, and day-wearied sun—
>
> *King John*, V, 4, 33-35.

> threw up their sweaty night-caps, and uttered such a deal of stinking breath because Cæsar refus'd the crown, that it had almost choked Cæsar; for he swooned and fell down at it.
>
> *J. C.*, I, 2, 244-247.

> Breath infect breath,
> That their society, as their friendship, may
> Be merely poison!
>
> *Timon*, IV, 1, 30-32.

Long may they kiss each other, for this cure!
O, never let their crimson liveries wear!
And as they last, their verdure still endure,
To drive infection from the dangerous year!
That the star-gazers, having writ on death,
May say, the plague is banish'd by thy breath.

Venus and Adonis, verse 85.

Shakespeare's contemporary dramatists shared this view of the infected breath.

O, your breath:
Out upon sweetmeats, and continued physic—
The plague is in them!

The White Devil, II, 1, 163-165.

Face.   The house, sir, has been visited.

Lovewit.   What, with the plague? stand thou then farther.

Face.   No, sir, I had it not.

Lovewit.   Who had it then? I left
None else but thee in the house.

Face.   Yes, sir, my fellow,
The cat that kept the buttery, had it on her
A week before I spied it; but I got her
Convey'd away in the night: and so I shut
The house up for a month—

Lovewit.   How!

Face.   Purposing then, sir,
T' have burnt rose-vinegar, treacle, and tar,
And have made it sweet, that you should ne'er have known it;
Because I knew the news would but afflict you, sir.

Lovewit.   Breathe less, and farther off!

The Alchemist, V, 1.

The Sun and the Moon exerted their separate influences on the presence of diseases:

All the infections that the sun sucks up
From bogs, fens, flats, on Prosper fall, and make him
By inch-meal a disease!

Tempest, II, 2, 1-3.

Worse than the sun in March,
This praise doth nourish agues.

1 Henry IV, IV, 1, 111-112.

You nimble lightnings, dart your blinding flames
Into her scornful eyes. Infect her beauty,
You fen-suck'd fogs, drawn by the pow'rful sun
To fall and blast her pride.

Lear, II, 4, 163-166.

O blessed breeding sun, draw from the earth
Rotten humidity.

Timon, IV, 3, 1-2.

Therefore the moon, the governess of floods,
Pale in her anger, washes all the air,
That rheumatic diseases do abound.

M. N. D., II, 1, 103-105.

It is to be noted, as Dover Wilson has so vividly recorded, [1] that

> Bodily ablutions and sanitation are inventions of nineteenth century England: a contemporary doctor advises his readers to confine their washing to the hands and wrists, to the face, the eyes, and the teeth, adding 'in the night, let the windows of your house, specially of your chamber, be closed.' Fresh air and sunlight were thought positively dangerous, ladies wearing masks to preserve their faces from the latter. Hygiene was in its infancy; the nostrums of medieval physic in their dotage, and physiology was based upon the notion of humours which goes back to Hippocrates. In a word, man living in a pre-scientific age had no clue either to the prevention or to the cure of disease, with the result that the streets stank like middens, which indeed they were, and bubonic plague was an annual visitant to the city. The danger of infection was, however, well recognised, and when the deaths from plague reached more than fifty a week the theatres were closed by authority.

As for the modern campaign for 'Clean Air', consider the difficulties the authorities of Elizabethan England had when faced with the recorded opinion of one man of that day on

---

[1] Wilson, J. Dover, *The Essential Shakespeare*, pp. 32-34.

the housing problem: William Harrison who wrote the *Description of England* in Holinshed's *Chronicle* (1577-1587), [1] finds the use of oak in the building of private houses a sign of the decay of morality:

'In times past men were contented to dwell in houses builded of sallow, willow, plumtree, hardbeame, and elme, so that the use of oke was in a manner dedicated wholie unto churches, religious houses, princes palaces, noblemens lodgings, and navigation; but now all these are rejected, and nothing but oke anie whit regarded. And yet see the change, for when our houses were builded of willow, then had we oken men; but now that our houses are come to be made of oke, our men are not onlie become willow, but a great manie through Persian delicacie crept in among us altogether of straw, which is a sore alteration. In those, the courage of the owner was a sufficient defense to keepe the house in safetie; but now the assurance of the timber, double doores, lockes and bolts, must defend the man from robbing. Now have we manie chimnies, and yet our tenderlings complaine of rheumes, catarhes, and poses. Then had we none but reredosses, and our heads did never ake. For as the smoke in those daies was supposed to be a sufficient hardning for the timber of the house, so it was reputed a far better medicine to keepe the goodman and his familie from the quacke or pose, wherewith as then verie few were oft acquainted.'

[1] Raleigh, Sir Walter, *Shakespeare's England*, I, Ch. I, p. 12.

Chapter Thirteen

SHAKESPEARE ON PREGNANCY

THE familiar and recurring miracle of pregnancy, from conception to the onset of labour and delivery, was the subject of frequent comment by the Elizabethan dramatists. Shakespeare's references to it are of the country-man's folk-lore type, but the expression of his knowledge is uniquely that of his own genius. Almost all aspects of preg-nancy are mentioned and they fit as naturally into the plays as, no doubt, they did into the everyday experience of Shake-speare's own life.

The secret hopes of every bride are expressed by Shakespeare as every bride would like to hear them; and what better wish could wedding-guests have, but never tactfully express?

> Now, until the break of day,
> Through this house each fairy stray.
> To the best bride-bed will we,
> Which by us shall blessed be;
> And the issue there create
> Ever shall be fortunate.
>
> . . . .
>
> And the blots of Nature's hand
> Shall not in their issue stand;
> Never mole, hare-lip, nor scar,
> Nor mark prodigious, such as are
> Despised in nativity,
> Shall upon their children be.

M. N. D., V, 1, 390-403.

There was no apparent desire amongst the Elizabethans to restrict the numbers in families.

> with immodest hatred
> The child-bed privilege denied, which 'longs
> To women of all fashion.

The Winter's Tale, III, 2, 100-102.

214

> almost at fainting under
> The pleasing punishment that women bear.
>
> . . . .
>
> There had she not been long but she became
> A joyful mother of two goodly sons.
>
> *C. of E.*, I, 1.

Shakespeare's ideas of conception were expressed in the terms of a countryman, naturally and inimitably:

> Your brother and his lover have embraced:
> As those that feed grow full—as blossoming time,
> That from the seedness the bare fallow brings
> To teeming foison,—even so her plenteous womb
> Expresseth his full tilth and husbandry.
>
> *M. for M.*, I, 4, 40-44.

> Look in thy glass, and tell the face thou viewest
> Now is the time that face should form another;
> Whose fresh repair if now thou not renewest,
> Thou dost beguile the world, unbless some mother,
> For where is she so fair whose unear'd womb
> Disdains the tillage of thy husbandry.
>
> *Sonnet*, 3.

or, in a plain statement of unembellished fact:

> Hymen hath brought the bride to bed,
> Where, by the loss of maidenhead,
> A babe is moulded.
>
> *Per.*, III, Introd., 9-11.

The difference in the views of Capulet and Lady Capulet about the right age for Juliet's marriage may be merely part of the story, but it may also reflect the changing views of the times. Early betrothals and marriages were common in Elizabethan times. Capulet was certainly justified in his plea.

> *Capulet.* My child is yet a stranger in the
> world;
> She hath not seen the change of fourteen years:
> Let two more summers wither in their pride
> Ere we may think her ripe to be a bride.

> *Paris.*   Younger than she are happy mothers
> made.
> *Capulet.*   And too soon marr'd are those so early
> made.
> > *R. & J.*, I, 2, 8-13.

> Well, think of marriage now.   Younger than you
> Here in Verona, ladies of esteem,
> Are made already mothers.   By my count,
> I was your mother much upon these years
> That you are now a maid.
> > *R. & J.*, I, 3, 70-74.

The signs and symptoms of pregnancy are noted by most Elizabethan dramatists, but Shakespeare's references are unique in his use of the unusual word, or in the sheer poetry of his imagery.   His contemporaries are more factual.

> The poor wench is cast away: she's quick; the child brags in her belly already.
> > *L. L. L.*, V, 2, 665-666.

'Brags' is an unusual word for foetal movements, but medically so very apt.

> When we have laugh'd to see the sails conceive
> And grow big-bellied with the wanton wind;
> Which she, with pretty and with swimming gait
> Following,—her womb then rich with my young squire,—
> Would imitate, and sail upon the land,
> To fetch me trifles, and return again,
> As from a voyage, rich with merchandise.
> > *M. N. D.*, II, 1, 128-134.

Two contemporary dramatists suffice to illustrate the difference in the quality of their references.

> *Margery.*   No, faith, Firk; no, perdy, Hodge.
> I do feel honour creep upon me, and which is more, a certain rising in my flesh; but let that pass.
> *Firk.*   Rising in your flesh do you feel, say you?   Ay, you may be with child, but why should not my master feel a rising in his flesh, having a gown and a gold ring on?   But you are such a shrew, you'll soon pull him down.
> > *The Shoemaker's Holiday*, III, 1, 175-181.

> *Bosola.*   I observe your duchess
> Is sick a days, she pukes, her stomach seethes,
> The fins of her eyelids look most teeming blue,
> She wanes i' th' cheek and waxes fat i' th' flank,
> And, contrary to our Italian fashion,
> Wears a loose bodied gown: there's somewhat in't.
> I have a trick may chance discover it,
> A pretty one; I have brought some apricocks,
> The first our spring yields.
> > *The Duchess of Malfi*, II, 1, 44-52.

Of the more advanced state of pregnancy, Shakespeare makes an observation, which is very true, about the effect of such women in a crowd, but I do not know that it has been made before or since.

> > Great bellied women,
> That had not half a week to go, like rams
> In the old time of war, would shake the press,
> And make 'em reel before 'em.
> > *H. VIII*, IV, 1, 76-79.

Webster is also acutely observant about a woman at full term.

> *Duchess.*   Your arm, Antonio: do I not grow
> >   fat?
> I am exceeding short-winded.—Bosola,
> I would have you, sir, provide for me a litter;
> Such a one as the Duchess of Florence rode in.
> *Bosola.*   The Duchess used one when she was
> >   great with child.
> *Duchess.*   I think she did.—Come hither, mend
> >   my ruff;
> Here, when?
> Thou art such a tedious lady; and thy breath smells
> Of lemon-peels; would thou hadst done! Shall I swoon
> Under thy fingers! I am so troubled
> With the mother!
> > *The Duchess of Malfi*, II, 1, 122-132.

(By most authorities 'the mother' is accepted as meaning hysteria, but in my view the sense here would be more accurately given as 'palpitation').

15

During pregnancy some women have an abnormal and compelling longing for unusual or out-of-season types of food. Shakespeare's contemporaries, especially Marlowe and Webster, tend to make great play of this peculiarity; but, as one comes to expect, Shakespeare merely uses the fact briefly to fit naturally into part of an image he has created. Marlowe explains the peculiarity quite explicitly.

> *Faustus.* I have heard that great-bellied women do long for some dainties or other: what is it, madam? tell me, and you shall have it.
>
> *Duchess.* Thanks, good Master Doctor: and, for I see your courteous intent to pleasure me, I will not hide from you the thing my heart desires; and, were it now summer, as it is January and the dead time of the winter, I would desire no better meat than a dish of ripe grapes.
>
> *Doctor Faustus.*

Webster elaborates the point, using it as a piece of detection in a dramatic denouement which his audience would quickly appreciate.

> *Duchess.*   For me, sir?
>
> *Bosola.* Apricocks, madam.
>
> *Duchess.* Oh, sir, where are they?
>
> *Bosola.* [*Aside*] Good; her colour rises.
>
> *Duchess.* Indeed, I thank you: they are wondrous fair ones.
> What an unskilled fellow is our gardiner!
> We shall have none this month.
>
> *Bosola.* Will not your grace pare them?
>
> *Duchess.* No: they taste of musk, methinks; indeed they do.
>
> *Bosola.* I know not: yet I wish your grace had pared 'em.
>
> *Duchess.* Why?
>
> *Bosola.* I forgot to tell you, the knave gardiner,
> Only to raise his profit by them sooner,
> Did ripen them in horse-dung.

Duchess.   O, you jest.—
You shall judge: pray taste one.

Antonio.   Indeed, madam,
I do not love the fruit.

Duchess.   Sir, you are loath
To rob us of our dainties: 'tis a delicate fruit;
They say they are restorative.

Bosola.   'Tis a pretty art,
This grafting.

Duchess. 'Tis so; a bettering of nature.

Bosola. To make a pippin grow upon a crab,
A damson on a blackthorn.—[*Aside*] How greedily she eats
them!
A whirlwind strike off these bawd farthingales!
For, but for that and the loose-bodied gown,
I should have discovered apparently
The young springal cutting a caper in her belly.

Duchess. I thank you, Bosola: they were right good
          ones,
If they do not make me sick.

Antonio.   How now, madam?

Duchess. This green fruit and my stomach are not
          friends:
How they swell me!

Bosola. [*Aside*] Nay, you are too much swelled already,

Duchess. Oh, I am in an extreme cold sweat!

Bosola. I am very sorry.

Duchess. Lights to my chamber!—O good Antonio,
I fear I am undone!

Delio. Lights, there, lights!

Antonio. O my trusty Delio, we are lost!
I fear she's fallen in labour; and there's left
No time for her remove.

Delio.   Have you prepar'd
Those ladies to attend her? and procur'd
That politic safe conveyance for the midwife
Your duchess plotted?

Antonio. I have.

Delio. Make use, then, of this forc'd occasion:
Give out that Bosola hath poison'd her
With these apricocks; that will give some colour
For keeping her close.

Antonio. Fie, fie, the physicians
Will then flock to her.

Delio. For that you may pretend
She'll use some prepared antidote of her own,
Lest the physicians should re-poison her.

Antonio. I am lost in amazement: I know not what to
think on't.

Bosola. So, so, there's no question but her tetchiness and
most vulturous eating of the apricocks are apparent signs
of breeding.

The Duchess of Malfi, II, 1, 143-185.

But Shakespeare uses his knowledge of this peculiarity merely
to add a little authenticity to the story which Pompey is
telling the magistrate.

Sir, she came in great with child; and longing, saving your
honour's reverence, for stew'd prunes. Sir, we had but two in
the house, which at that very distant time stood, as it were, in a
fruit dish, a dish of some three pence; your honours have seen
such dishes; they are not China dishes, but very good dishes.

M. for M., II, 1, 86-91.

The folk-lore beliefs about pregnancy are well illustrated
in Shakespeare's comments about Gloucester, e.g. the
influence a woman's thoughts during pregnancy may exert
on her child, or the significance of the manner of delivery of
the child. The superstitious Elizabethan audience believed
in these things and would accept their implications without
question.

Why, love forswore me in my mother's womb:
And, for I should not deal in her soft laws,
She did corrupt frail nature with some bribe,
To shrink mine arm up like a wither'd shrub;

To make an envious mountain on my back,
Where sits deformity to mock my body;
To shape my legs of an unequal size;
To disproportion me in every part,
Like to a chaos, or an unlick'd bear whelp
That carries no impression like the dam.

3 *H. VI*, III, 2, 153-162.

Thy mother felt more than a mother's pain,
And yet brought forth less than a mother's hope;
To wit, an indigested and deformed lump,
Not like the fruit of such a goodly tree.
Teeth hadst thou in thy head when thou wast born,
To signify thou camest to bite the world.

3 *H. VI*, V, 6, 49-54.

I, that have neither pity, love, nor fear.
Indeed, 'tis true, that Henry told me of;
For I have often heard my mother say
I came into the world with my legs forward.
Had I not reason, think ye, to make haste,
And seek their ruin that usurp'd our right?
The midwife wonder'd, and the women cried
'O, Jesus bless us, he is born with teeth!'
And so I was; which plainly signified
That I should snarl and bite and play the dog.
Then, since the heavens have shap'd my body so.
Like hell make crook'd my mind to answer it.

3 *H. VI*, V, 6, 68-79.

I—that am curtail'd of this fair proportion,
Cheated of feature by dissembling nature,
Deform'd, unfinish'd, sent before my time
Into this breathing world scarce half made up,
And that so lamely and unfashionable
That dogs bark at me as I halt by them.

R. III, I, 1, 18-23.

Only Ben Jonson, of the contemporaries studied, refers to this, and he does so twice.

You were born with a cawl on your head.

The Alchemist, I, 1.

For my particular, I can, and from a most clear conscience,
affirm, that I have ever trembled to think toward the least
profaneness; have loathed the use of such foul and unwashed
bawdry, as is now made the food of the scene; and, howsoever
I cannot escape from some, the imputation of sharpness, but
that they will say, I have taken a pride, or lust, to be bitter, and
not my youngest infant but hath come into the world with all
his teeth.

Volpone (from the dedication).

The pains of labour are only briefly referred to by Shakespeare; and there are no comparable references by his contemporaries.

> But that I am as well begot, my liege,—
> Fair fall the bones that took the pains for me!
> Compare our faces and be judge yourself.
>
> *K. John*, I, 1, 77-79.

> Thy mother felt more than a mother's pain,
> And yet brought forth less than a mother's hope.
>
> 3 *H. VI*, V, 6, 49-50.

> Now hath my soul brought forth her prodigy,
> And I, a gasping new-deliver'd mother,
> Have woe to woe, sorrow to sorrow join'd.
>
> *R. II*, II, 2, 63-65.

> Turn all her mother's pains and benefits
> To laughter and contempt.
>
> *Lear*, I, 4, 286-287.

> Lucina, O!
> Divinest patroness, and midwife gentle
> To those that cry by night, convey thy deity
> Aboard our dancing boat; make swift the pangs
> Of my queen's travails!
>
> *Pericles*, III, 1, 10-14.

Delivery by Cæsarean section is mentioned in the well-known:

> *Macbeth.* I bear a charmed life, which must not
>   yield
> To one of woman born.

> *Macduff.*   Despair thy charm,
> And let the angel whom thou still hast served
> Tell thee, Macduff was from his mother's womb
> Untimely ripp'd.
>
>   *Macbeth*, V, 8, 12-16.

The midwife is used in one example of Shakespeare's medical imagery.

> So, Green, thou art the midwife to my woe,
> And Bolingbroke my sorrow's dismal heir.
>
>   *R. II*, II, 2, 61-62.

The birth of the illegitimate child is twice the subject of comment.

> Upon his death-bed he by will bequeath'd
> His lands to me, and took it on his death
> That this my mother's son was none of his;
> And if he were, he came into the world
> Full fourteen weeks before the course of time.
>
>   *K. John*, I, 1, 109-113.

> *Kent.* Is this your son, my lord?
>
> *Gloucester.* His breeding, sir, hath been at my charge: I have so often blushed to acknowledge him that now I am braz'd to't.
>
> *Kent.* I cannot conceive you.
>
> *Gloucester.* Sir, this young fellow's mother could: whereupon she grew round-wombed, and had indeed, sir, a son for her cradle ere she had a husband for her bed.
>
>   *Lear.* I, 1, 7-14.

It is an interesting speculation—but no more than that—whether Shakespeare knew of the possible effects of syphilis in pregnancy, when he wrote the speech for Henry VIII in the divorce scene.

> First, methought
> I stood not in the smile of heaven, who had
> Commanded nature that my lady's womb,
> If it conceived a male-child by me, should
> Do no more offices of life to't than
> The grave does to the dead; for her male issue
> Or died where they were made, or shortly after
> This world had air'd them.
>
>   *H. VIII*, II, 4, 186-193.

Sterility caused as much concern among the Elizabethans as it does to-day. Shakespeare refers to it on three occasions:

> Forget not in your speed, Antonius,
> To touch Calpurnia; for our elders say,
> The barren, touched in this holy chase,
> Shake off their sterile curse.
>
> *J. V.*, I, 2, 6-9.

> Hear, nature, hear; dear goddess, hear!
> Suspend thy purpose, if thou dost intend
> To make this creature fruitful:
> Into her womb convey sterility:
> Dry up in her the organs of increase,
> And from her derogate body never spring
> A babe to honour her!
>
> *Lear*, I, 4, 275-281.

Fie, fie upon her! she is able to freeze the god Priapus, and undo a whole generation; we must either get her ravished, or be rid of her.

> *Pericles*, IV, 6, 3-5.

The menopause is mentioned only once by Shakespeare, and not at all by his contemporaries. Here, as in his reference to conception, Shakespeare returns to the pure poetry of the countryman:

> Have we more sons, or are we like to have?
> Is not my teeming date drunk up with time?
>
> *R. II*, V, 2, 90-91.

Chapter Fourteen

SHAKESPEARE ON CHILDREN

Now, until the break of day,
Through this house each fairy stray.
To the best bride-bed will we,
Which by us shall blessed be;
And the issue there create
Ever shall be fortunate.
So shall all the couples three
Ever true in loving be;
And the blots of Nature's hand
Shall not in their issue stand;
Never mole, hare lip, nor scar,
Nor mark prodigious, such as are
Despised in nativity,
Shall upon their children be.

M. N. D., V, 1, 39-403.

NOTHING in Shakespeare so readily arouses the sympathy of the audience, or the reader, as his references to Children. He succeeds at once in establishing a universal appeal which no one can resist, least of all the women in the audience. Sometimes it is done by evoking the idea of the helplessness of babies and children.

Yet the incessant weepings of my wife,
Weeping before for what she saw must come,
And piteous plainings of the pretty babes,
That mourn'd for fashion, ignorant what to fear—

C. of E., I, 1, 73-74.

At first the infant,
Mewling and puking in the nurse's arms.
Then the whining schoolboy, with his satchel
And shining morning face, creeping like snail
Unwillingly to school.

A.Y.L., II, 7, 143-147.

It is yours;
And, might we lay the old proverb to your charge,
So like you, 'tis the worse. Behold, my lords,
Although the print be little, the whole matter
And copy of the father, eye, nose, lip;
The trick of 's frown; his forehead; nay, the valley,
The very mould and frame of hand, nail, finger:
And thou, good goddess Nature, which hast made it
So like him that got it, if thou hast
The ordering of the mind too, 'mongst all colours
No yellow in't, lest she suspect, as he does,
Her children not her husband's!

Winter's Tale, II, 3, 95-107.

His passion is so ripe it needs must break.
And when it breaks, I fear will issue thence
The foul corruption of a sweet child's death.

King John, IV, 2, 79-81.

My lord, I was born about three of the clock in the afternoon,
with a white head, and something a round belly.

2 H. IV, I, 2, 176-177.

But I am weaker than a woman's tear,
Tamer than sleep, fonder than ignorance,
Less valiant than the virgin in the night,
And skilless as unpractised infancy.

T. & C., I, 1, 9-12.

set on you
To wake our peace, which is our country's cradle
Draws the sweet infant breath of gentle sleep.

R. II, I, 3, 131-133.

Sleep she as sound as careless infancy.

Merry Wives, V, 5, 50.

He does it, too, by the image of the baby-nurse relationship.

Fie, fie, how wayward is this foolish love,
That like a testy babe will scratch the nurse,
And presently, all humbled, kiss the rod!

T. G. of V., I, 2, 57-59.

Peace, peace!
Dost thou not see my baby at my breast
That sucks the nurse asleep?

A. & C., V, 2, 306-308

Or like the froward infant still'd with dandling,
He now obeys, and now no more resisteth.

Venus and Adonis, 5, 94.

He does it particularly in his account of how Juliet was weaned, a description too often overlooked or forgotten even by those who know the play well.

'Tis since the earthquake now eleven years;
And she was wean'd,—I never shall forget it—
Of all the days of the year, upon that day:
For I had then laid wormwood to my dug,
Sitting in the sun under the dove-house wall;
My lord and you were then at Mantua;—
Nay, I do bear a brain:—but, as I said,
When it did taste the wormwood on the nipple
Of my dug, and felt it bitter, pretty fool,
To see it tetchy, and fall out with the dug!

R. & J., I, 3, 24-33.

None of the contemporary dramatists with whom I have attempted comparison show anything of Shakespeare's over-flowing sympathy in his references to children. Indeed, in the plays considered, there are only three very commonplace references to children.

Faith, the child hath a sweet breath, George; but I think it be troubled with worms; carduus benedictus and mare's milk were the only thing in the world for't.

Knight of the Burning Pestle, III, 3, 27-30.

You were born with a cawl on your head.

The Alchemist, I, 1.

and not my youngest infant but hath come into the world with all his teeth!

Volpone (the dedication).

Indeed, it required the magic and genius of Shakespeare to produce that immortal picture of the baby:

To bed, to bed; sleep kill those pretty eyes,
And give as soft attachment to thy senses
As infants' empty of all thought!

T. & C., IV, 2, 4-6.

Chapter Fifteen

SHAKESPEARE ON OLD AGE

S HAKESPEARE is always sympathetic in his serious
descriptions of Old Age. The clinical picture arouses in
the audience or the reader the feelings of pathos, the
inevitability of man's destiny, and, perhaps, too, in recognising this, something of self-pity.

> Not know my voice! O time's extremity,
> Hast thou so crack'd and splitted my poor tongue
> In seven short years that here my only son
> Knows not my feeble key of untun'd cares?
> Though now this grained face of mine be hid
> In sap-consuming winter's drizzled snow,
> And all the conduits of my blood froze up,
> Yet hath my night of life some memory,
> My wasting lamps some fading glimmer left,
> My dull deaf ears a little use to hear;
> All these old witnesses—I cannot err—
> Tell me thou art my son Antipholus.
>
> C. of E., V, 1, 306-317.

> Let me be your servant:
> Though I look old, yet I am strong and lusty;
> For in my youth I never did apply
> Hot and rebellious liquors in my blood,
> Nor did not with unbashful forehead woo
> The means of weakness and debility;
> Therefore my age is as a lusty winter,
> Frosty, but kindly. Let me go with you;
> I'll do the service of a younger man
> In all your business and necessities.
>
> As You Like It, II, 3, 46-55.

> The sixth age shifts
> Into the lean and slipper'd pantaloon,
> With spectacles on nose and pouch on side.
> His youthful hose, well sav'd, a world too wide
> For his shrunk shank; and his big manly voice,

Turning again toward childish treble, pipes
And whistles in his sound. Last scene of all
That ends this strange eventful history,
Is second childishness, and mere oblivion,
Sans teeth, sans eye, sans taste, sans every thing.

As You Like It, II, 7, 157-166.

Kind keepers of my weak decaying age,
Let dying Mortimer here rest himself.
Even like a man new haled from the rack,
So fare my limbs with long imprisonment;
And these grey locks, the pursuivants of death,
Nestor-like aged in an age of care,
Argue the end of Edmund Mortimer.
These eyes, like lamps whose wasting oil is spent,
Wax dim, as drawing to their exigent;
Weak shoulders, overborne with burdening grief,
And pithless arms, like to a wither'd vine
That droops his sapless branches to the ground.
Yet are these feet, whose strengthless stay is numb,
Unable to support this lump of clay,
Swift-winged with desire to get a grave,
As witting I no other comfort have.

1 *H. VI*, II, 5, 1-16.

A good leg will fall; a straight back will stoop; a black beard
will turn white; a curl'd pate will grow bald; a fair face will
wither; a full eye will wax hollow. But a good heart, Kate, is
the sun and the moon; or, rather, the sun and not the moon—
for it shines bright and never changes, but keeps his course truly.

H. V, V, 2, 155-162.

Slanders, sir: for the satirical rogue says here that old men have
grey beards; that their faces are wrinkled; their eyes purging
thick amber and plum-tree gum; and that they have a plentiful
lack of wit, together with most weak hams—all which, sir,
though I most powerfully and potently believe, yet I hold it
not honesty to have it thus set down; for you yourself, sir, shall
grow old as I am, if, like a crab, you could go backward.

Hamlet, II, 2, 195-202.

Were I hard-favour'd, foul, or wrinkled-old,
Ill-nurtured, crooked, churlish, harsh in voice,
O'erworn, despised, rheumatic and cold,
Thick-sighted, barren, lean, and lacking juice,
   Then mightest thou pause, for then I were not for thee;
   But having no defects, why dost thou abhor me?
Venus and Adonis, 23.

In her the painter had anatomized
Time's ruin, beauty's wreck, and grim care's reign:
Her cheeks with chaps and wrinkles were disguised;
Of what she was no semblance did remain:
Her blue blood changed to black in every vein,
   Wanting the spring that those shrunk pipes had fed,
   Show'd life imprison'd in a body dead.
The Rape of Lucrece, 208.

But when he is pointing fun at the old man with young ideas, he can be quite ruthless in his scorn of the embarrassing spectacle.

Prince. Swearest thou, ungracious boy? Henceforth ne'er look on me. Thou art violently carried away from grace; there is a devil haunts thee in the likeness of an old fat man; a tun of man is thy companion. Why dost thou converse with that trunk of humours, that bolting-hutch of beastliness, that swoll'n parcel of dropsies, that huge bombard of sack, that stuff'd cloak bag of guts, that roasted Manningtree ox with the pudding in his belly, that reverend vice, that grey iniquity, that father ruffian, that vanity in years? Wherein is he good, but to taste sack and drink it? Wherein neat and cleanly, but to carve a capon and eat it? wherein cunning, but in craft? wherein crafty, but in villany? wherein villanous, but in all things? wherein worthy, but in nothing?

Falstaff. I would your grace would take me with you; whom means your grace?

Prince. That villanous abominable misleader of youth, Falstaff, that old white-bearded Satan.
1 *H. IV*, II, 4, 430-448.

Falstaff. You that are old consider not the capacities of us that are young; you do measure the heat of your livers with the bitterness of your galls; and we that are in the vaward of our youth, I must confess, are wags too.

Chief Justice. Do you set down your name in the scroll of youth, that are written down old with all the characters of age? Have you not a moist eye, a dry hand, a yellow cheek, a white beard, a decreasing leg, an increasing belly? Is not your voice broken, your wind short, your chin double, your wit single, and every part about you blasted with antiquity? And will you yet call yourself young? Fie, fie, fie, Sir John!

2 H. IV, I, 2, 160-175.

A man can no more separate age and covetousness than 'a can part young limbs and lechery; but the gout galls the one, and the pox pinches the other; and so both the degrees prevent my curses.

2 H. IV, I, 2, 215-219.

Prince. Look whe'er the wither'd elder hath not his poll claw'd like a parrot.

Poins. Is it not strange that desire should so many years outlive performance?

2 H. IV, II, 4, 248-251.

> You cannot call it love; for at your age
> The heyday in the blood is tame, it's humble,
> And waits upon the judgment.

Hamlet, III, 4, 68-70.

> These old fellows
> Have their ingratitude in them hereditary.
> Their blood is caked, 'tis cold, it seldom flows;
> 'Tis lack of kindly warmth they are not kind;
> And nature, as it grows again toward the earth,
> Is fashion'd for the journey, dull and heavy.

Timon, II, 2, 214-219.

> And then, forsooth, the faint defects of age
> Must be the scene of mirth; to cough and spit
> And, with a palsy-fumbling on his gorget,
> Shake in and out the rivet. And at this sport
> Sir Valour dies; cries 'O, enough, Patroclus;
> Or give me ribs of steel! I shall split all
> In pleasure of my spleen.'

T. & C., I, 3, 172-178.

He recognises that there can be no compromise between the outlooks of 'crabbed age and youth'.

Crabbed age and youth cannot live together:
Youth is full of pleasaunce, age is full of care;
Youth like summer morn, age like winter weather;
Youth like summer brave, age like winter bare.
Youth is full of sport, age's breath is short;
  Youth is nimble, age is lame;
Youth is hot and bold, age is weak and cold;
  Youth is wild, and age is tame.
Age, I do abhor thee; youth, I do adore thee.

The Passionate Pilgrim, 12.

Only one of his contemporaries, Ben Jonson, in the present study, shows anything approaching Shakespeare's sympathy to the aged.

So many cares, so many maladies,
So many fears attending on old age,
Yea, death so often call'd on, as no wish
Can be more frequent with them, their limbs faint,
Their senses dull, their seeing, hearing, going,
All dead before them; yea, their very teeth,
Their instruments of eating, failing them:
Yet this is reckon'd life! nay, here was one,
Is now gone home, that wishes to live longer!
Feels not his gout, nor palsy; feigns himself
Younger by scores of years, flatters his age
With confident belying it, hopes he may,
With charms, like Aeson, have his youth restored:
And with these thoughts so battens, as if fate
Would be as easily cheated on, as he,
And all turns air!

Volpone, I, 1.

By the briefest of brilliant touches, Shakespeare can evoke the pathos of old age.

Care keeps his watch in every old man's eye,
And where care lodges sleep will never lie.

R. & J., II, 3, 35-36.

The oldest hath borne most; we that are young
Shall never see so much nor live so long.

Lear, V, 3, 325-326.

Chapter Sixteen

SHAKESPEARE ON EYES

SHAKESPEARE was acutely and accurately observant about eyes, and he used his knowledge to stir the sympathy of his audience with very telling effect. He can, at once produce our profound sympathy for the loss of sight:

He that is strucken blind cannot forget
The precious treasure of his eyesight lost.
                                                      R. & J., I, 1, 230-231.

Hubert.   None, but to lose your eyes.
Arthur.   O heaven! that there were but a mote in
                  yours,
A grain, a dust, a gnat, a wandering hair,
Any annoyance in that precious sense;
Then feeling what small things are boisterous there,
Your vile intent must needs seems horrible.
                                                      King John, IV, 1, 92-96.

All Shakespeare's references to eyes are, of course, of medical interest, but those of the greatest value—they are also the most numerous—are the ones which even to-day have a clinical application. They reveal a power of observation characteristic and distinctive of Shakespeare. Nothing like them is found in the writings of his contemporaries.

For I do see the cruel pangs of death
Right in thine eye.
                                                      King John, V, 4, 59-60.

His eye is hollow, and he changes much.
                                                      2 *H. IV*, IV, 5, 6.

A good leg will fall; a straight back will stoop; a black beard will turn white; a full eye will wax hollow.
                                                      H. V, V, 2, 158-160.

Do you note
How much her grace is alter'd on the sudden?
How long her face is drawn! how pale she looks,
And of an earthly cold! Mark her eyes!

She is going, wench: pray, pray.

H. VIII, IV, 2, 95-99.

What a hate looks through his eyes! So should he look
That seems to speak things strange.

Macbeth, I, 2, 47-48.

Avaunt, and quit my sight. Let the earth hide thee.

Thy bones are marrowless, thy blood is cold;
Thou hast no speculation in those eyes
Which thou dost glare with.

Macbeth, III, 4, 93-96.

You see, her eyes are open.

Ay, but their sense is shut.

Macbeth, V, 1, 24-25.

Admirable: how this grace
Speaks his own standing! what a mental power
This eye shoots forth! how big imagination
Moves in this lip! to the dumbness of the gesture
One might interpret.

Timon of Athens, I, 1, 32-37.

The inter-relation and the interdependence of the senses interested Shakespeare.

Dark night, that from the eye his function takes,
The ear more quick of apprehension makes;
Wherein it doth impair the seeing sense,
It pays the hearing double recompense.
Thou art not by mine eye, Lysander found;
Mine ear, I thank it, brought me to thy sound.

M. N. D., III, 2, 177-182.

Mine eyes smell onions.

All's Well, V, 3, 314.

Fool. Thou canst tell why one's nose stands i' the middle on 'is face?

Lear.   No.

Fool. Why, to keep one's eyes of either side's nose, that what a man cannot smell out he may spy into.

Lear, I, 5, 19-22.

All that follow their noses are led by their eyes but blind men; and there's not a nose among twenty but can smell him th t's stinking.

Lear, II, 4, 68-70.

> Then I best my tabor;
> At which, like unback'd colts, they prick'd their ears,
> Advanced their eyelids, lifted up their noses
> As they smelt music.

Tempest, IV, 1, 175-178.

> Eyes without feeling, feeling without sight,
> Ears without hands or eyes, smelling sans all,
> Or but a sickly part of one true sense
> Could not so mope.

Hamlet, III, 4, 78-81.

Shakespeare explains why, traditionally, Cupid is always blind.

> Love looks not with the eyes, but with the mind;
> And therefore is wing'd Cupid painted blind.

M. N. D., I, 1, 234-235.

Don Pedro. I shall see thee, ere I die, look pale with love.

Benedick. With anger, with sickness, or with hunger, my lord; not with love; prove that ever I lose more blood with love than I will get again with drinking, pick out mine eyes with a ballad-maker's pen, and hang me up at the door of a brothel-house for a sign of blind Cupid.

Much Ado, I, 1, 214-219.

His note on double vision is of clinical interest.

> Methinks I see these things with parted eye,
> When every thing seems double.

M. N. D., IV, 1, 186-187.

Shakespeare uses the effect of the appearance of the eyes to convey tragedy:

> Beaufort's red sparkling eyes blab his heart's malice,
> And Suffolk's cloudy brow his stormy hate;

> Sharp Buckingham unburdens with his tongue
> The envious load that lies upon his heart.
>
> 2 H. VI, III, 1, 154-157.

or a teasing comedy:

> Now show the wound mine eye hath made in thee:
> Scratch thee but with a pin, and there remains
> Some scar of it; lean but upon a rush,
> The cicatrice and capable impressure
> Thy palm some moment keeps; but now mine eyes,
> Which I have darted at thee, hurt thee not,
> Nor, I am sure, there is no force in eyes
> That can do hurt.
>
> As You Like It, III, 5, 20-27.

But Shakespeare's most remarkable comment on eyes is his ingenious scene of *The Miracle*.

[*Enter a Townsman of Saint Albans, crying 'A Miracle'.*]

> *Gloucester.* What means this noise?
> Fellow, what miracle dost thou proclaim?
>
> *Townsman.* A miracle! a miracle!
>
> *Suffolk.* Come to the King, and tell him what
>   miracle.
>
> *Townsman.* Forsooth, a blind man at Saint Albans
>   shrine
> Within this half hour hath receiv'd his sight;
> A man that ne'er saw in his life before.
>
> *King.* Now God be prais'd that to believing souls
> Gives light in darkness, comfort in despair!

[*Enter the Mayor of Saint Albans and his Brethren, bearing Simpcox between two in a chair; his wife and a multitude following.*]

> *Cardinal.* Here comes the townsmen on procession
> To present your Highness with the man.
>
> *King.* Great is his comfort in this earthly vale,
> Although by his sight his sin be multiplied.
>
> *Gloucester.* Stand by, my masters; bring him near
>   the King;
> His Highness' pleasure is to talk with him.

King. Good fellow, tell us here the circumstance,
That we for thee may glorify the Lord.
What, hast thou been long blind and now restor'd?

Simpcox. Born blind, an't please you Grace.

Wife. Ay, indeed was he.

Suffolk. What woman is this?

Wife. His wife, an't like your worship.

Gloucester. Hadst thou been his mother, thou
  couldst have better told.

King. Where wert thou born?

Simpcox. At Berwick in the north, an't like your
  Grace.

King. Poor soul, God's goodness hath been great
  to thee.
Let never day nor night unhallowed pass,
But still remember what the Lord hath done.

Queen. Tell me, good fellow, cam'st thou here by
  chance,
Or of devotion, to this holy shrine?

Simpcox. God knows, of pure devotion; being call'd
A hundred times and oft'ner, in my sleep,
By good Saint Alban, who said 'Simpcox, come,
Come, offer at my shrine, and I will help thee.'

Wife. Most true, forsooth; and many times and oft
Myself have heard a voice to call him so.

Cardinal. What, art thou lame?

Simpcox. Ay, God Almighty help me!

Suffolk. How cam'st thou so?

Simpcox. A fall off of a tree.

Wife. A plum tree, master.

Gloucester. How long hast thou been blind?

Simpcox. O, born so, master!

Gloucester. What, and wouldst climb a tree?

Simpcox. But that in all my life, when I was a youth.

Wife. Too true; and bought his climbing very dear

Gloucester. Mass, thou lov'dst plums well, that
            would venture so.

Simpcox. Alas, good master, my wife desir'd some
          damsons,
And made me climb, with danger of my life.

Gloucester. A subtle knave! But yet it shall not serve:
Let me see thine eyes; wink now; now open them;
In my opinion yet thou seest not well.

Simpcox. Yes, master, clear as day, I thank God and
          Saint Alban.

Gloucester. Say'st thou me so? What colour is this
            cloak of?

Simpcox. Red, master; red as blood.

Gloucester. Why, that's well said. What colour is my
            gown of?

Simpcox. Black, forsooth; coal-black as jet.

King. Why, then, thou know'st what colour jet is
       of?

Suffolk. And yet, I think, jet did he never see.

Gloucester. But cloaks and gowns before this day a
            many.

Wife. Never before this day in all his life.

Gloucester. Tell me, sirrah, what's my name?

Simpcox. Alas, master, I know not.

Gloucester. What's his name?

Simpcox. I know not.

Gloucester. Nor his?

Simpcox. No, indeed, master.

Gloucester. What's thine own name?

Simpcox. Saunder Simpcox, an' if it please you,
          master.

Gloucester. Then, Saunder, sit there, the lying'st knave
in Christendom. If thou hadst been born blind, thou
mightst as well have known all our names as thus to name
the several colours we do wear. Sight may distinguish of

colours; but suddenly to nominate them all, it is impossible.
My lords, Saint Alban here hath done a miracle; and would
ye not think it cunning to be great that could restore this
cripple to his legs again?

Simpcox. O master, that you could!

Gloucester. My masters of Saint Albans, have you not
beadles in your town, and things call'd whips?

Mayor. Yes, my lord, if it please your Grace.

Gloucester. Then send for one presently.

Mayor. Sirrah, go fetch the beadle hither straight.

[*Exit an Attendant.*

Gloucester. Now fetch me a stool hither by and by.

[*A stool brought.*

Now, sirrah, if you mean to save yourself from whipping,
Leap me over this stool and run away.

Simpcox. Alas, master, I am not able to stand alone!
You go about to torture me in vain.

[*Enter a Beadle with whips.*

Gloucester. Well, sir, we must have you find your legs.
Sirrah beadle, whip him till he leap over that same stool.

Beadle. I will, my lord. Come on, sirrah; off with your
doublet quickly.

Simpcox. Alas, master, what shall I do? I am not able
to stand.

[*After the Beadle hath hit him once, he leaps over the stool and runs
away; and they follow and cry, 'A miracle.'*]

2 *H. VI*, II, 1.

No reference to eyes of any medical interest were found in
the plays studied of Shakespeare's contemporaries.

Chapter Seventeen

SHAKESPEARE ON THE EAR, NOSE
AND THROAT

AS one would expect in a man of the theatre, Shakespeare was interested in the sense of hearing and in voice production; nor is it surprising that in the London of his day, he was constantly reminded of his sense of smell. All three are referred to frequently.

The Ear. Examples of deafness used in his imagery are:

> High-stomach'd are they and full of ire,
> In rage, deaf as the sea, hasty as fire.
>> *R. II*, I, 1, 18-19.

> You breathe these dead news in as dead an ear.
>> *John*, V, 7, 65.

> for pleasure and revenge
> Have ears more deaf than adders to the voice
> Of any true decision.
>> *T. & C.*, II, 2, 171-173.

> My liege, her ear
> Is stopp'd with dust: the first of April died
> Your noble mother.
>> *John*, IV, 2, 119-121.

> Though Richard my life's counsel would not hear,
> My death's sad tale may yet undeaf his ear.
>> *R. II*, II, 1, 15-16.

The lack of concentration and inattention of old age—the quickly tiring hearing sense—is referred to:

> aged ears play truant at his tales,
> And younger hearings are quite ravished.
>> *L. L. L.*, II, 1, 74-75.

The effect of fatigue and illness on hearing is mentioned several times and evokes one of the most memorable quotations from Shakespeare:

Life is as tedious as a twice-told tale
Vexing the dull ear of a drowsy man.

> *John*, III, 4, 108-109.

The falling cadence alone of these lines is suggestively sleep-provoking.

> sickly ears,
> Deaf'd with the clamours of their own dear groans.

> *L. L. L.*, V, 2, 851-852.

O, then I see that madmen have no ears.
How should they, when that wise man have no eyes?

> *R. & J.*, III, 3, 61-62.

Cæsar's deafness is mentioned.

Come on my right hand, for this ear is deaf,
And tell me truly what thou think'st of him.

> *J.C.*, I, 2, 213-214.

Open you ears; for which of you will stop
The vent of hearing when loud Rumour speaks?

> *H. IV* (2), Induction, 1-2.

O that men's ears should be
To counsel deaf, but not to flattery!

> *Timon*, I, 2, 251-252.

Dost thou hear?
Your tale, sir, would cure deafness.

> *Tempest*, I, 2, 105-106.

You cram these words into mine ears against
The stomach of my sense.

> *Tempest*, II, 1, 100-101.

It was the nightingale, and not the lark,
That pierc'd the fearful hollow of thine ear.

> *R. & J.*, III, 5, 2-3.

The apparent increased acuity of hearing in the dark is noted and its correct explanation given.

Dark night, that from the eye his function takes,
The ear more quick of apprehension makes;
Wherein it doth impair the seeing sense,
It pays the hearing double recompense.

Thou art not by mine eye, Lysander, found;
Mine ear, I thank it, brought me to thy sound.

M. N. D., III, 2, 177-182.

It might even be imagined that Shakespeare knew of the possibilities of suggestion under narcosis:

But I will find him when he lies asleep,
And in his ear I'll holla 'Mortimer'.

H. IV (1) I, 3, 221-222.

Falstaff's attempt at the deafness of the malingerer deserves to be quoted in full.

Falstaff. Boy, tell him I am deaf.

Page. You must speak louder; my master is deaf.

Chief Justice. I am sure he is, to the hearing of anything good.

. . . .

Falstaff. An't please your lordship, I hear his Majesty is return'd with some discomfort from Wales.

Chief Justice. I talk not of his Majesty. You would not come when I sent for you.

Falstaff. And I hear, moreover, his Highness is fall'n into this same whoreson apoplexy.

Chief Justice. Well, God mend him! I pray you let me speak with you.

Falstaff. This apoplexy, as I take it, is a kind of lethargy, an't please your lordship, a kind of sleeping in the blood, a whoreson tingling.

Chief Justice. What tell you me of it? Be it as it is.

Falstaff. It hath it original from much grief, from study, and perturbation of the brain. I have read the cause of his effects in Galen; it is a kind of deafness.

Chief Justice. I think you are fall'n into the disease, for you hear not what I say to you.

Falstaff. Very well, my lord, very well. Rather an't please you, it is the disease of not listening, the malady of not marking, that I am troubled withal.

Chief Justice. To punish you by the heels would amend the attention of your ears; and I care not if I do become your physician.

Falstaff. I am as poor as Job, my lord, but not so patient. Your lordship may minister the potion of imprisonment to me in respect of poverty; but how should I be your patient to follow your prescriptions, the wise may make some dram of a scruple, or indeed a scruple itself.

H. IV (2) I, 2.

There are references to giddiness, which results from an upset of the organ of balance in the inner ear.

Turn giddy, and be holp by backward turning.

R. & J., I, 2, 47.

He that is giddy thinks the world turns round.

The Shrew, V, 2, 20.

I am giddy; expectation whirls me round.

T. & C., III, 2, 17.

All three expressions show a keen, accurate, clinical descriptive power. 'Whirls', also used by Ben Jonson (*vide infra*), is particularly apposite since it conveys the forceful, compelling and irresistible sensation which the patient experiences in the true labyrinthine storm.

THE NOSE.

The Fool's reason for the position of the nose adds one more function to that organ.

Fool. Thou can'st tell why one's nose stands i' the middle on's face?

Lear. No.

Fool. Why, to keep one's eyes of either side's nose, that what a man cannot smell out, he may spy into.

Lear, I, 5, 19-22.

Later the Fool adds a further comment.

All that follow their noses are led by their eyes but blind

men; and there's not a nose among twenty but can smell
him that's stinking.

Lear, II, 4, 68-70.

The sense of smell, which was no doubt lively and overworked
in the streets of Shakespeare's day, has three references.

By the Lord, a buck-basket! Ramm'd me in with foul
shirts and smocks, socks, foul stockings, greasy napkins,
that, Master Brook, there was the rankest compound of
villainous smell that ever offended nostril.

Merry Wives, III, 5, 80-83.

Turn then my freshest reputation to
A savour that may strike the dullest nostril
Where I arrive, and my approach be shunn'd,
Nay, hated too, worse than the greatest infection
That e'er was heard or read.

Winter's Tale, I, 2, 420-424.

But the most remarkable of all Shakespeare's medical references is his terse comment on the sense of smell. In four words
it epitomises all that has ever been written about reflex action
and the conditioned reflexes.

Mine eyes smell onions.

All's Well, V, 3, 314.

There are two references to nasal intonation in speech.

Some men there are love not a gaping pig;
Some that are mad if they behold a cat;
And others, when the bagpipe sings i' th' nose,
Cannot contain their urine.

M. of V., IV, 1, 47-50.

Why, masters, ha your instruments been in Naples, that
they speak i' th' nose thus?

Othello, III, 1, 3-4.

The method of testing the patency of the nasal airways by a
wisp of cotton-wool was in vogue even in Shakespeare's time.

By his gates of breath
There lies a downy feather which stirs not.
Did he suspire, that light and weightless down
Perforce must move.

H. IV (2), IV, 5, 31-34.

> Lend me a looking-glass;
> If that her breath will mist or stain the stone,
> Why, then she lives.
>
> . . . .
>
> This feather stirs; she lives.
>
> *Lear*, V, 3, 261-263: 265.

Among the references to diseases of the nose are:

> Do thou amend thy face, and I'll amend my life.
> Thou art our admiral, thou bearest the lantern in the
> poop, but 'tis in the nose of thee; thou art the Knight of
> the Burning Lamp.
>
> *H. IV* (1), III, 3, 24-27.

The Hippocratic facies.

> After I saw him fumble with the sheets, and play with
> flowers, and smile upon his fingers' end, I knew there was
> but one way; for his nose was as sharp as a pen, and a'
> babbl'd of green fields.
>
> *H. V*, II, 3, 15-18.

Syphilis of the Nose.

> Down with the nose,
> Down with it flat, take the bridge quite away
> Of him that, his particular to foresee,
> Smells from the general weal.
>
> *Timon*, IV, 3, 156-159.

The next reference to the nose may be either to the common cold or to nasal catarrh. But it is not to the actual nasal condition that I want to refer. I want rather to note that here Shakespeare uses a medical situation at a most poignant and intensely dramatic moment in the play.

> I have a salt and sorry rheum offends me;
> Lend me thy handkerchief.
>
> *Othello*, III, 4, 48-49.

Desdemona cannot produce the handkerchief and Othello's worst suspicions are confirmed. This, it is interesting to note, is one of many occasions in the tragedies when Shakespeare uses a medical situation to intensify the pathos or heighten the dramatic effect.

THE LARYNX.

The first reference is to a condition which would be of great concern to Shakespeare and his boy actors. The 'breaking' of the boy's voice would naturally mean the end of his career in a woman's part in the play.

> Speak between the change of man and boy
> With a reed voice; and turn two mincing steps
> Into a manly stride.
>
> *M. of V.*, III, 4, 66-68.

The effect of emotion on the voice:

> Speak, Winchester; for boiling choler chokes
> The hollow passage of my poison'd voice,
> By sight of these our baleful enemies.
>
> *H. VI* (1), V, 4, 120-122.

The effect of illness on the voice:

> More would I, but my lungs are wasted so
> That strength of speech is utterly denied me.
>
> *H. IV* (2), IV, 5, 217-218.

Shakespeare shows a true understanding of the psychological background to the temperament of indifferent singers.

> Shall we clap into't roundly, without hawking or spitting
> or saying we are hoarse, which are the only prologues to
> a bad voice?
>
> *As You Like It*, V, 3, 9-11.

Shakespeare's contemporaries occasionally refer to the ear, nose and throat and amongst the references the following are found.

> *Lightborn.* You shall not need to give instructions;
> 'Tis not the first time I have kill'd a man:
> I learn'd in Naples how to poison flowers;
> To strangle with a lawn thrust down the throat;
> To pierce the windpipe with a needle's point;
> Or, whilst one is asleep, to take a quill,
> And blow a little powder in his ears;
> Or open his mouth, and pour quick-silver down.
>
> *Edward the Second.*

Follow your grave instructions; give them words;
Pour oil into their ears, and send them hence.

Volpone, I, 1.

This intemperate noise
Fitly resembles deaf men's shrill discourse,
Who talk aloud, thinking all other men
To have their imperfection.

Duchess of Malfi, II, 5, 51-54.

Our drink shall be prepared gold and amber;
Which we will take, until my roof whirl round
With the vertigo.

Volpone, III, 5.

Nose, nose, jolly red nose,
And who gave thee this jolly red nose?
Nutmegs and ginger, cinnamon and cloves;
And they gave me this jolly red nose.

Knight of the Burning Pestle, I, 4, 47-53.

My nose bleeds,
One that were superstitious would count
This ominous, when it merely comes by chance:
Two letters, that were wrought here for my name,
Are drown'd in blood!

Duchess of Malfi, II, 3, 41-45.

Sir, against one o'clock prepare yourself;
Till when you must be fasting; only take
Three drops of vinegar in at your nose,
Two at your mouth, and one at either ear;
Then bathe your fingers' ends and wash your eyes,
To sharpen your five senses, and cry 'hum'
Thrice, and then 'buz' as often; and then come.

The Alchemist, I, 1.

His nose is like a common sewer, still running.

Volpone, I, 1.

My mother's death hath mortified my mind,
And sorrow stops the passage of my speech.

Tamburlaine the Great (2), III, 2.

Chapter Eighteen

SHAKESPEARE AND THE VENEREAL DISEASES

SHAKESPEARE, like all other Elizabethans, was well aware of the effects of the venereal diseases—the maladies of France. He used his knowledge of them in at least seven of his plays, sometimes in a serious way and sometimes in a frankly bawdy manner. Bawdiness in the Elizabethan theatre reflected the life not merely of the groundlings outside the theatre: it was a healthy, robust type of humour, just as the age was healthy and robust in its outlook on life. It was not a squeamish age, and puritan prudery had no place in the theatre.

The land and the houses of the theatre district in London in Shakespeare's day were part of the diocese of the Bishop of Winchester. The brothels were in this area and they were known as 'the Winchester stews'. Their inhabitants were 'the Winchester geese', and they were, no doubt, the prototypes of Doll Tearsheet and Mistress Overdone. There was at that time no mystery about how the diseases were spread.

Lucio. Behold, behold, where Madam Mitigation comes! I have purchas'd as many diseases under her roof as come to—

2nd Gent. To what, I pray?

1st Gent. Judge.

2nd Gent. To three dolours a year.

1st Gent. Ay, and more.

Lucio. A French crown more.

1st Gent. Thou art always figuring diseases in me; but thou art full of error; I am sound.

Lucio. Nay, not, as one would say, healthy; but so sound as things that are hollow; thy bones are hollow; impiety has made a feast of thee.

Measure for Measure, 1, 2.

248

Boult. But, mistress, do you know the French knight that
cowers i' th' hams?

Bawd. Who? Monsieur Veroles?

Boult. Ay, he; he offered to cut a caper at the proclamation;
but he made a groan at it, and swore he would see her to-morrow.

Bawd. Well, well; as for him, he brought his diseases hither:
here he does but repair it. I know he will come in our shadow to
scatter his crowns in the sun.

Pericles, IV, 2.

> *Marina.*   For me
> That am a maid, though most ungentle fortune
> Hath placed me in this sty, where, since I came,
> Diseases have been sold dearer than physic.

Pericles, IV, 6.

Thersites. After this, the vengeance on the whole camp! or,
rather, the Neapolitan bone-ache! for that, methinks, is the curse
depending on those that war for a placket.

Troilus and Cressida, II, 3.

> *Timon.* Be a whore still; they love thee not that
>   use thee.
> Give them diseases, leaving them with their lust.
> Make use of thy salt hours. Season the slaves
> For tubs and baths; bring down rose-cheek'd youth
> To the tub-fast and the diet.

Timon of Athens, IV,3.

The 'tub-fast and the diet', of course, referred to the treatment
of venereal diseases in Elizabethan times. 'The powdering
tub of infamy' was, in fact, a tub in which the patient was
exposed to fumes from powder of cinnabar. This powder
was thrown on to a hot-plate or a chafing-dish, and was
volatilised, condensing as a powder on the patient's body.
Ambroise Paré and the Elizabethan surgeons, Clowes and
Woodall, preferred inunction, but they write of mercurial
fumigation as if it were in common use. Woodall writes,
'Sinnabar, which is used in fumes for the pox, is a deadly
medicine, half made of quicksilver, and half of brimstone by
art of fire.' Clowes describes mercurial fumigation by means

17

'of certain trocheses or perfumes; the patient being placed under a canapie or pavilion in which the trocheses (of cinnabar and gums) are burnt on a chafing dish of coals'. Paré records that 'some have devised a fourth manner of curing the "lues venerea", which is suffitus or fumigations. They put the patient under a tent or canopy made close on every side, lest any thing should expire, and they put in unto him a vessel with hot coals, whereupon they plentifully throw cinnabaris, so that they may on every side enjoy the rising fume'. In another chapter he describes 'a barrel fitted to receive the fumes in'—'You may put the patient naked into the barrel, so that he may sit upon a seate or board perforated, thus the patient shall easily receive the fume that exhales and none of it be lost, he covering and venting himself on every side'. 'Sweating-houses' were still in existence in London in the time of Charles I, and were located in Leather Lane in Holborn; they may even have spread over into Hatton Garden.

Other places of treatment, the 'spital houses', were also available.

> *Pistol.* O hound of Crete, think'st thou my spouse
>   to get?
> No; to the spital go,
> And from the powd'ring tub of infamy
> Fetch forth the lazar kite of Cressid's kind,
> Doll Tearsheet she by name, and her espouse.
>
> *Henry V*, II, 1.

> *Pistol.* News have I that my Nell is dead i' th' spital
> Of malady of France.
>
> *Henry V*, V, 1.

The effects of the various types of venereal disease were not clearly differentiated; they were all due to the 'pox'. Falstaff twice mentions his difficulty in distinguishing between the gout and the pox.

> *Falstaff.* A man can no more separate age and covetousness

than a' can part young limbs and lechery; but the gout galls
the one, and the pox pinches the other; and so both the degrees
prevent my curses.

2 Henry IV, I, 2.

Falstaff. A pox of this gout! or, a gout of this pox! for the
one or the other plays the rogue with my great toe. 'Tis no
matter if I do halt; I have the wars for my colour, and my
pension shall seem the more reasonable. A good wit will make
use of anything. I will turn diseases to commodity.

2 Henry IV, I, 2.

A more serious consequence would seem to be revealed by
Henry VIII.

> Henry.   First, methought
> I stood not in the smile of heaven, who had
> Commanded nature that my lady's womb,
> If it conceiv'd a male child by me, should
> Do no more offices of life to't than
> The grave does to the dead; for her male issue
> Or died where they were made, or shortly after
> This world had air'd them.

Henry VIII, II, 4.

No more vivid clinical picture of the tertiary stage of
syphilis has ever been written than when Timon advises the
two courtesans on how to take their revenge on men. No
doubt Shakespeare was recording what was in his day a
common enough sight; but happily how rare it is to-day!

> Timon.   Consumptions sow
> In hollow bones of man; strike their sharp shins,
> And mar men's spurring. Crack the lawyer's voice,
> That he may never more false title plead,
> Nor sound his quillets shrilly. Hoar the flamen,
> That scolds against the quality of flesh
> And not believes himself. Down with the nose,
> Down with it flat, take the bridge quite away
> Of him that, his particular to foresee,
> Smells from the general weal. Make curl'd-pate ruffians bald,
> And let the unscarr'd braggarts of the war

Derive some pain from you. Plague all,
That your activity may defeat and quell
The source of all erection. There's more gold.
Do you damn others, and let this damn you,
And ditches grave you all!

Timon of Athens, IV, 3.

Chapter Nineteen

MEDICAL REFERENCES IN SHAKESPEARE

THE line references are from 'The Tudor Shakespeare Edition', edited by PETER ALEXANDER, Collins, 1951.

1. *The Tempest*

Act I, Sc. 1, line 43-45
       Sc. 2, line 105-106
              325-326
              363-365
              369-370
Act II, Sc. 1, line 100-101
               132-133
               182-187
        Sc. 2, line 1-3
               38
Act III, Sc. 3, line 43-47
Act IV, Sc. 1, line 156-163
               171-183
               191-192
               258-260

2. *The Two Gentlemen of Verona*

Act I, Sc. 1, line 2
       Sc. 2, line 57-59
Act II, Sc. 1, line 33-36
Act V, Sc. 4, line 71-72

3. *The Merry Wives of Windsor*

Act II, Sc. 3, line 26-27
Act III, Sc. 1, line 94
        Sc. 3, line 169
        Sc. 5, line 12-16
               17-20
               80-83

Act V, Sc. 5, line 9-14
              50
              146

4. *Measure for Measure*

Act I, Sc. 2, line 43-56
       Sc. 4, line 40-44
              77-83
Act II, Sc. 1, line 86-87
        Sc. 2, line 134-136
Act III, Sc. 1, line 2-3
               5-41
               79-82
               119-133
Act IV, Sc. 6, line 7-8
Act V, Sc. 1, line 277-278

5. *The Comedy of Errors*

Act I, Sc. 1, line 46-47
              50-51
              73
Act II, Sc. 2, line 71-72
Act V, Sc. 1, line 68-86
              98-105
              236-248
              306-317

6. *Much Ado About Nothing*

Act I, Sc. 1, line 70-74
              206-219
       Sc. 3, line 5-15

Sc. 4, line 275-289
299-301
Sc. 5, line 18-23
Act II, Sc. 4, line 68-70
104-110
163-166
220-224
Act III, Sc. 2, line 35-36
Sc. 4, line 8-9
11-14
33-35
Sc. 7, line 105-106
Act V, Sc. 2, line 60-61
Sc. 4, line 1-14
Sc. 6, line 170-172
Sc. 7, line 14-25
Act V, Sc. 3, line 121-122
260-263
265
272-273
325-326

34. Othello

Act I, Sc. 3, line 308-310
320-331
Act II, Sc. 1, line 96-159
Sc. 3, line 358-359
Act III, Sc. 1, line 3-4
Sc. 3, line 334-337
Sc. 4, line 49-50
104-107
146-149
Act IV, Sc. 1, line 33-55

35. Antony and Cleopatra

Act I, Sc. 5, line 4-5
7-18
73-74

Act II, Sc. 1, line 20-27
Sc. 2, line 239-244
Sc. 6, line 97-98
Act III, Sc. 2, line 4-6
Sc. 13, line 195-200
Act IV, Sc. 7, line 7-9
Sc. 9, line 11-23
Sc. 15, line 21-29
Act V, Sc. 1, line 35-37
Sc. 2, line 58-60
291-296
306-307
341-353

36. Cymbeline

Act I, Sc. 4, line 129-130
Sc. 5, line 1-43
Act II, Sc. 5, line 1-35
Act III, Sc. 4, line 111-114
186-190
Act IV, Sc. 2, line 259-282
Act V, Sc. 5, line 28-31

37. Pericles

Act I, Sc. 2, line 67-69
Act III, Intro. line 9-11
Sc. 1, line 10-14
Sc. 2, line 31-48
Act IV, Sc. 2, line 105-115
Sc. 6, line 3-10
13-15
94-101
163-171

38. Sonnets

Sonnet III line 1-6
XXXIV line 5-8

INDEX